WATER TALKS

WATER TALKS

EMPOWERING COMMUNITIES TO KNOW, RESTORE, AND PRESERVE THEIR WATERS

Betsy Damon

Foreword by

Dr. Jane Goodall, DBE

Portalbooks ≈ 2022

Portalbooks

An imprint of Anthroposophic Press / SteinerBooks
PO Box 58, Hudson, NY 12534
www.steinerbooks.org

Unless noted otherwise, illustrations are by Molly McIntyre, except: p. 13 *Man in bottle* is by Raoul Anchondo; p. 20 *Color illustration* is by Betsy Damon; p. 160 *Bioindicators illustration* is by Raoul Anchondo; p. 173 *Trees illustration* is by Betsy Damon, as are the background drawings on the title page and at the beginning of each chapter.

LIBRARY OF CONGRESS CONTROL NUMBER: 2021952246

ISBN: 978-1-938685-38-5 (paperback)

Contents

ACKNOWLEDGEMENTS

Dedicated to my granddaughters,
Anja Keblish Damon
and
Anora Zhang Otto

I could never have written this book without the support of many. Most of the projects covered in this book were created in, and by, communities of people who came together.

Words are not enough to express how grateful I am for my family: for my son John Otto and Zhang Xuehua, without whom much of my work in China would never have happened; for my daughter Tamara Damon and son-in-law Gary Keblish, who gave me their constant support in writing this book over the past four years. My sister Tammy Damon read the first drafts and urged me to write more. My brother George read various pieces, especially the ending, many times over.

Inspired by Jane Goodall, I served on the board of her organization, Roots & Shoots, for three years in Beijing. I experienced her down-to-earth brilliance and frank, kind responses to challenges. I saw her weave together her passion to protect chimpanzees with her work educating future generations worldwide through the Roots & Shoots program.

I founded Keepers of the Waters (keepersofthewaters.org) in 1991 to support those working to restore earth's living systems. All the while, a book lingered in the back of my mind. In 2017, the idea was launched at a Keepers of the Waters board meeting at Linda Weintraub's exceptional space in Rhinebeck, New York. A year later, I gathered a small group together for four days to outline the book: Colin and Carol Franklin, who slept on the studio floor for three nights; Margot Young, who slept on a sofa; and Lauren Brady, an intern from Bennington College. Ivy Halderman, my assistant, moved everything along with her organizational skills. Many others helped pull this book together: Will Simpson, Raoul Anchando, Tom Roberts-McMichael, and Annabel Roberts-McMichael.

Marion R. Weber's unqualified support allowed me to go to China. Marion has continued to be a rock of support to this day. Sustained funding from the Kalliopeia Foundation allowed me to dive deep into water and community. I'd like to give a special thank-you to Layla Forrest-White, the indispensable editor who helped me integrate everything in this book, and to Lynne Elizabeth, whose immense generosity informed this book in its final stages. Molly McIntyre, a neighborhood artist, generously created most of the cartoons. We met at the Tin Cup Cafe, our local coffee shop. Finally, my studio assistant Margot McMahon helped with organization and proofreading.

This list cannot capture what is to be held in community by activists and artists, friends and neighbors. Above all, to those whose confidence in me was greater than my confidence in myself: thank you.

FOREWORD

Dr. Jane Goodall, DBE

Since I first met Betsy in Beijing, some twenty years ago, she has been obsessed—in the best possible way—with water. Her love for it, her concern about what we humans are doing to it—polluting it, damming it, draining it, wasting it, disrespecting it—led to her writing this book. *Water Talks* is based on science but filled with the spirit of the artist. It reflects her passion for knowledge and her love, not just for the subject she writes about, but for water itself, in all its beauty and complexity. During our many meetings, we have shared our feelings of distress about the lack of understanding of the true nature of water, its importance, and its vulnerability.

Her visuals are unique and her story carries the reader along ever deeper into water. Threaded throughout the book is the perspective that water must be a human right and that all life is interdependent with water. Betsy has created a "Toolkit" that intends to empower everyone to take steps to understand their waters and organize to protect and restore their waters. This is a very accessible book. It is grounded in practical processes that can enable a community to understand the best local choices for the place they live in.

At the time of writing, I have lived on Planet Earth for eighty-three years. I have seen so much change, and that includes advances in living standards for millions of people on the one hand, and the increasing destruction of the environment on the other. Somehow, we must find a middle path. This is why Betsy wrote this book. All people need to be empowered to know their waters and to take charge of lifesaving decisions.

I cannot remember a time when I did not love water. During my Cambridge days, I went out in a canoe on the River Cam at least two evenings a week. I would pull in under the branches of a weeping willow and, alone in the green tree cave, watch with endless fascination the moving, living water. I thought of Shakespeare, who found "books in the running brooks," and remembered Kenneth Grahame's immortal book *The Wind in the Willows*, with its enchanting descriptions of the river—as when Mole sat on the bank, while "the river chattered on to him, a babbling procession of the best stories in the world, sent from the heart of the earth to be told at last to the insatiable sea." Indeed, literature, along with art and music, can make poetry of the hard facts of science and appeal to the heart as well as the head so that a wider range of people become interested and involved.

It is not surprising that water deities and the worship of water have been woven into myths for thousands of years. Where did it begin, our deep, spiritual connection with water? In Gombe National Park, deep in the forest, there is a small, but magnificent waterfall. It drops some eighty feet from a high rocky outcrop to the streambed below. Over the eons, it has worn a deep channel in the rocks, and ferns and vines move ceaselessly in the breeze created by the falling water. From the start, I sensed great spiritual power in this place.

Sometimes when a group of chimpanzees approaches the falls and hears the roaring of the falling water, they show signs of excitement, their hair bristles, and their pace quickens. This is the start of an amazing "waterfall display." It is a ritual. They move upright in the streambed, swaying rhythmically from foot to foot, picking up and throwing rocks, leaping to seize the hanging vines and swing out into the spray-drenched wind. After about five minutes it is over, and one of them may sit on a rock, his eyes following the movement of the water as it crashes down, then flows on past him. What is this living "thing" that is always coming, always moving away, yet always right there with him? If chimpanzees could speak with words, discuss what must surely be a sense of wonder, of awe, might not this lead to an early animistic religion, the worship of a mystery of nature? It was only later that I learned that this place had been a sacred site for the people who used to live in the valleys of Gombe, a place where the elders would gather at certain times of year to perform their secret rites.

In this book, Betsy tells the story of her thirty-five years as an artist/activist for water, her successes, and her discouragement as she watched water sites further degrade. Consistently she expresses confidence that humans can come together to solve our many challenges—that basically we will and we must do this.

I have personally witnessed the gradual changes that have occurred in Africa. It was in 1960 that I first arrived at Gombe National Park on the shore of that longest and second deepest freshwater lake in the world, Lake Tanganyika. The water was crystal clear. You could see fish swimming on the sandy bottom at least twenty feet below. But gradually this changed. As trees were cut down on the steep valley slopes, the heavy rains of the wet season washed the soil down into the streams that flowed out into the lake in ever greater clouds of red-brown mud. And as the human population of the lakeside towns grew, pollution from small businesses and human and livestock waste also found its way into the lake. Visitors who did not see the water fifty years ago praise its clarity. Many of the great rivers of Africa have been contaminated with pollution from industrial, agricultural and household chemicals washed into the rivers during the rainy season and the mercury used when panning for gold.

Of course, there have always been problems with water. People have wanted or have been forced to live and farm in places where there was not enough rain or groundwater, and fighting over water rights has often been fierce. It was in 650 BC that the Chinese philosopher Lao Tzu said that the "wise leader solves the problems of water first." For many years now, as human populations grow around the globe, we have been warned that the next wars will be fought over water. It might be hard for some to live without oil and gas, but no one can survive without water.

Climate change is leading to more problems. Droughts are succeeding each other year after year, so that in many developing countries traditional herders are having to leave their way of living, as their livestock dies of thirst and starvation. And hundreds of thousands of wild animals are dying, too.

"Water, water everywhere nor any drop to drink" laments the Ancient Mariner in the epic poem of Samuel Taylor Coleridge as his vessel, becalmed for days, lies "idle as a painted ship upon a painted ocean." Will we, in our desperation to increase supplies of freshwater, desalinate more and more of the oceans? And what will that do? So what *can* we do about this increasingly grim situation? *Water Talks* contains inspiring moments and successes of people and communities that have organized around saving a water place. It also provides rays of hope. Knowing that knowledge is empowering, Betsy has given us a toolkit of processes from Listening to Mapping to Designing for Complexity and Resilience. This book contains solutions that every community can use to head themselves toward complexity, and resilience.

Let us get together, she urges, and each do our bit to educate each other, restore rivers, remove dams, dig up the cement that channels so many rivers and streams as they pass through our towns, free them from the cement beneath which we have imprisoned them. Restore wetlands. And, above all, value each drop of water we drink, do not take it for granted. A cup of water that we toss thoughtlessly down the sink would be worth its weight in gold to water-deprived people around the world.

Our real hope lies in young people. They are becoming more aware of the importance of the natural world, more concerned about the harm we are inflicting. Roots and Shoots, the Jane Goodall Institute's environmental and humanitarian education program for young people from preschool through university, allows its members—now in 100 countries—to choose, themselves, projects to make the world a better place for animals, people, and the environment. And many groups choose to do projects based on water—cleaning streams, writing to legislators, and learning about the true nature and the true value of this most precious of resources. This important book will surely stimulate many more such projects.

Thank you, Betsy, for all the love and hard work that has gone into creating this most important book.

Jane Goodall is considered the world's foremost expert on chimpanzees and best known for her sixty-year study of social and family interactions of wild chimpanzees, which began in 1960 in Gombe National Park, Tanzania. Her numerous books include *My Life with the Chimpanzees* (1998) and *Reason for Hope: A Spiritual Journey* (1999).

INTRODUCTION

We are drops,
Flowing as one river
Rising as mist
Floating as clouds
Sparkling as dew.
Remember.

As an artist, activist, and teacher, my creative curiosity has focused on water for forty years. I have explored water from the interior of the drop to the systems that function as the veins of the earth. I seek to invite people to know their waters, to be in relationship with each other, and to work within and across communities worldwide to repair the living system. My journey with water has opened my body, mind, and heart to a vast interconnectedness of living in a watery world.

In my search to understand water, I've come across spiritual practices of protection and healing, engineering solutions both ancient and modern, thousands of chemicals, pollution, filters, and infinite means for wastewater treatment, but very little about how those H_2O molecules really function. Although this knowledge is embedded in ancient, Indigenous, and ayurvedic cultures, it is only recently that "Western" scientists are approaching answers to some of the more existential questions about water: How exactly does water create life? What is the connection between water quality and a dynamic ecosystem? Above all, what *is* water?

The recent scientific understanding of the complex interconnectedness of living systems is a 180-degree turn from the perspective that disconnection is more scientific, practical and economical, and that we live in a dog-eat-dog world in which a straight river or straight line is seen as the perfect choice for control.

Most people know that water is three stages of the hydrologic cycle—the cycle through which water passes from clouds to precipitation and ice and back to clouds. But this does not begin to provide a real understanding of the profound function of water on Earth and in the universe. Until I decided to pay attention to water, I was not conscious of how water forms and informs every detail of existence.

My country, the United States, is a resource-rich country, where

we use water as if it were an unlimited resource. For many people, water flows from taps; toilets flush, and bathtubs fill up with the turn of a faucet. Water has been provided with ease. Many people notice water only as a monthly bill, or when a pipe breaks.

Over my eighty years, I have witnessed the decline in quality of almost every body of water I've known. We've treated rivers and lakes as our dumping sites. A vast and unregulated bottling industry has taken over, public water fountains have vanished, and water is now the new gold, being rapidly privatized. Simultaneously, the knowledge that water quality matters for all life has evaporated.

An aerial view of a river system closely resembles the veins and arteries of the human body. When speaking to an audience, I often ask: How many veins and arteries can be moved or removed from the body before it will die? We have moved and removed the veins of rivers to such an extent that whole water systems are rendered ineffective. Like our blood, rivers nourish and feed living systems. They cleanse and discharge unwanted substances. Like our veins and arteries, they don't work if they are overloaded with pollution, dammed too much, or transferred elsewhere.

Arteries and aerial view of a river system

Climate-related challenges, including increased tsunamis, hurricanes, tornadoes, and earthquakes, are impacting communities around the globe. Communities face problems ranging from too much water in the wrong place, to too little; from decaying and inadequate infrastructures, to dangerously polluted supplies. Every day, 150 to 200 species of plants, insects, birds, and mammals go extinct. Are there consequences to losing this biodiversity? Will it help to ensure that the water in which species thrive are not removed, drained, and polluted?

Natural forces—like meteors and earthquakes—have threatened life on earth for as long as it has existed. Earth has faced extinction events in the past. Yet this human-caused extinction event is unparalleled in its speed. One of the root causes of this mass extinction is damage to our life-sustaining water systems and forests.

Water science and technology have been vehicles of liberation and progress, providing benefits, especially in urban environments. Recently, we can effectively deliver water to millions of people, remove waste, and convert waste into byproducts. On the other hand, many natural water systems have been altered by dams, vast pipe systems, the destruction of wetlands and estuaries, and the transfer of water to supply cities. This, along with the extensive conversion of waterways into concrete ditches and pipes, has weakened the intrinsic resilience and flexibility of the earth's waters.

Ignoring water's essential role as the connective tissue of all life on earth is widespread. Unfortunately, the response to each environmental problem tends to be piecemeal—addressing one threat rather than responding with the complex solutions that will address the underlying problems. For instance, a river that has been straightened and restrained between flood walls cannot respond adequately to rising waters, nor can it distribute its waters into the surrounding landscape. Contributing streams to that river have been funneled into pipes that dump the water into the already stressed river, thus increasing flooding while depriving the land of water. To date, most solutions have been to address a single purpose, rather than engage with nature's complexity.

Single-Purpose Design

Although there are many contributing factors, single-purpose design is one of the main roots of the water crisis and climate crisis. Single-purpose design treats all development situations similarly, without regard for what is best—only for what is efficient from a short-term monetary perspective. Single-purpose design solves one problem without considering the impact on the surrounding land and ecosystems. An "efficient" design usually means easily controlled and disconnected from other systems.

Monsanto not only genetically engineers seeds; it also claims legal ownership of the seeds it has altered, leaving farmers to bear the burden of re-purchasing the rights to these seeds every year. This is a telling example of single-purpose design carried out to an extreme, threatening the very foundation of life.

Piecemeal responses to increasing climate chaos are enabled by the common misconception that there is little interconnectivity among parts of a complex system. Single-purpose design says: Slash all the trees, divide the land into parts, and build without regard for the land's capacity to sustain development. This refusal to engage in complexity is also fueled by the notion that a "one size fits all" approach is the most economical.

> *"You cannot solve a problem with the thinking that created it."*
> —ALBERT EINSTEIN

Water is the single enlivening element that we all depend on. We have boxed, dammed, and contained it. We must share this resource not only with each other but with all life. This consciousness gets lost when people hold water for personal gain. Finally, there are no national or international regulations to prevent companies and people from buying water sources anywhere in the world unless a country has decided to protect their waters. Throughout the world water sources are being bought and taken away from the places and peoples they have served throughout history.

Examples from our history reveal sharing and interdependence, not exploitation and isolation. In New Mexico, Indigenous tribes shared their water supplies in times of drought. I am sure there are many more similar cases.

We are a species that thrives in community, with vast interdependencies. Much of my early performance art required collaboration, and was generated from the upwelling of the collective of women meeting in consciousness-raising groups and supporting each other. My performance work from 1977 to 1987 was created by close-knit

groups in workshop settings. I am forever grateful that I was supported by so many people, and that I got to support so many people. Bringing people together—as individuals, yet committed to a unified purpose—became my model for projects. What does it mean to work in partnership with water instead of dominating it?

Our climate and water issues are a crisis of forgetting: We cannot take care of the foundation of life if we have forgotten that we exist because water is that foundation. More important, we can succeed only when communities, large and small, work together to restore interdependence, resilience, complexity, and flexibility to the earth's water systems and forests.

Water is self-regenerating when it's moving, when it's exposed to sun, air, and plant life and not overloaded with pollutants. Humans—you and I—also thrive moving in an alive world with sunlight and clean air.

Water offers us countless lessons for how to exist in complexity with each other. Water does not discriminate. It nourishes all life. Our communities are most innovative and powerful when everyone

is included. Diversity in community requires variety in many ways, including economic class, race, religion, skills, and knowledge. Complexity for water means that it moves through many varying situations: tumbling, bubbling, cruising slowly, eddying, living inside vast cavernous spaces, pouring out of a glacier and passing through reedy places, mangroves, and much more. Water does not naturally degrade; its degradation is a side effect of human negligence. It takes considerable effort to pollute a moving river or a large lake, just as it takes considerable effort to discourage the human spirit.

It is necessary that we have drinkable water and restore many systems soon. We must work on both the micro—our homes and communities—and the macro—the earth's shared ponds, streams, rivers, estuaries, and wetlands. To accomplish this, we need to understand certain fundamental information about water. Much of the basics, along with organizing tools, are included in this book. I detail many of my organizing principles, as well as challenges and successes from my forty years working at the intersection of art, science, and community.

My knowledge is empirical. It comes from listening, looking, researching a particular place, asking questions, learning the necessary science for that location, trying projects, and inviting many to work together. Above all I am logical, and logic likes truth. There is so much we do that is not logical. Who thought that concrete on every river was desirable, or that straightening rivers was better? What species pollutes the source of life?

This book is a mixture of my passion to know water and learn from it, new and exciting scientific information, and fundamental issues and processes that can help every community reclaim its waters. We need to build a worldwide public knowledge of methods for engaging communities, building teams, mapping, and revitalizing vast portions of earth. Water is shouting her many messages. She is our verb, our call to action.

Water is a humble, most common liquid, upon which all life depends. It is the sculptor of all forms. We need it every day to be alive. We are inexplicably drawn to the watery places, the ocean's edge, lakes, streams, falls, and springs. We are water beings and every cell in our bodies is 70% water.

The chapters provide general headings in which examples of what is needed and why are set alongside the projects or parts of projects in which those skills are useful. Every chapter contains visuals, not only from projects, but also cartoons that concisely illustrate the kinds of concepts that usually require heavier research.

This introduction offers an overview of **Water as a Human Right**, the right to life, and looks at issues such as privatization and bottling, which are challenging the reality that all life needs water.

We continue with **My Water Story**, and I invite readers to remember their own story. The personal is political, and we all have our own adventures and experiences with water. Each chapter is centered on what I find to be the foundations of acting for and with water, beginning with **Listening**, which is the foundation of learning from and being with water and people.

I place **Art** as the central creative initiative that can inspire and educate. Why is this so? Art envisions, and artists can imagine the impossible. Artists can imagine beyond the restraints of a discipline. The discipline of art is to imagine and apply skills.

Next is **Community**. Everyone lives in a community, even if they don't realize it. Water is the connective tissue of our communities, seen or unseen. Our communities thrive on their waters. In this chapter, I present many practical processes to bring people together, including a sample workshop. These are to assist with your thinking as you get to know your own community.

Mapping—I discovered that mapping is perhaps the most valuable tool for everyone in a community to have a clear understanding of their waters, their watershed, and what they can do. Maps reveal all the details needed to get started.

Water Balance—this is possibly the least understood aspect of our waters among the public. How much water is actually available in a community without a transfer and without taking more than our fair share of a river, lake, or aquifer?

Designs for Complexity and Resilience—In reality, an efficient design is one that reduces carbon, recycles water and waste, and builds toward resilience. An efficient design addresses complexity. For example, during a flood stage, a flexible river has plenty of places to overflow into, such as ponds along the river, wetlands, and healthy floodplains. This chapter presents designs for both the micro and macro levels.

Conclusion—Can we come together and decide to create a resilient and balanced system, not overused or overburdened with too much pollution? Can we work toward a system that contains sufficient complexity, interconnected systems, and a diversity of plant and animal species? A system is flexible when it can consistently adapt to new conditions.

Water as a Human Right

> *Water is a human right.*
> *Water is an earth right.*
> *Water is the right to life.*

The 1948 Universal Declaration of Human Rights states: "Everyone has the right to a standard of living adequate for the health and well-being of himself and his family, including food, clothing, housing."[1] What we can determine from this declaration is that water is a right, not a commodity. All life forms need water to survive, yet the necessity of a=-==nd dependence on water are often taken for granted.

At this moment in the twenty-first century, the earth faces many unprecedented challenges to its survival. The human population is growing exponentially, global water consumption is increasing, and climates are changing drastically due to global warming. We are facing the reality that healthy—or even drinkable—water is becoming a scarce resource. In 2010, in an attempt to combat this problem, the United Nations Ambassador to Bolivia, a country that has experienced the devastating effects of water privatization, boldly put forth a resolution declaring water as a human right. With the support of 122 countries, the United Nations passed Resolution 62/292, declaring water as a human right. The resolution states that "the human right to water entitles everyone to sufficient, safe, acceptable, physically accessible and affordable water for personal and domestic uses."[2]

Let's consider the implications of such a resolution: to declare a human right is to make governing bodies responsible for respecting, protecting, and guaranteeing that right. This means that under the 2010 UN Resolution, governments must provide their citizens access to safe and affordable water for personal and domestic use. Additionally, citizens need to be educated about their rights in order to hold their governments accountable. As more pressure is being put on our water resources, the duty of accountability is becoming increasingly important. Many countries, including the United States, Canada, and the United Kingdom, have yet to commit to the principle of water as a human right.

Unfortunately, water is being treated more and more as a profitable commodity, allowing the governments and companies in control of water resources to make money by exploiting a manufactured crisis of scarcity. But the human need for quality water is non-negotiable. To demand money for water is to demand money for life.

We need to democratize ownership of water and eliminate the ability to own other people's water. Every place, community, and country needs to be in charge of its water. This means making bodies of water the common property of all who live near it, which will require policies and practices generated from an understanding of our dependence on one another and nature.

When I bring a group together around water issues, a connection is automatic. There is buried in all of us a collective knowing about water. Not long ago in many cultures there was an active articu-
lation of water's essential role in sustaining life. Today, I have only found this in indigenous cultures. Imagine if this collective knowing were embedded in our contemporary culture, and became a part of our
teachings. Would we use waterways, rivers, and oceans as our sew-
ers? If we all knew that salmon return to the river in which they were born after as many as five years out at sea, would we continue to dam and destroy the rivers they depend on?

> *"If we surrendered to earth's intelligence,*
> *we could rise up rooted, like trees."*
> —Rainer Maria Rilke

As an Earth advocate, I envision a value system that is complex enough to help us properly care for and share this planet; a value system that understands our interdependence with the earth, and all her species. In my vision, clean water, air, and soil would be available for all life without a price tag. Pipelines would not cross through rivers, waters would belong to those who protect them, and the possibility of war over water would not exist. Throughout history, many cultures have encoded protections for water into daily life. Such respect for water is far more common in Indigenous cultures—cul-
tures that are often now on the front lines of fighting to keep their waters. When I visited Tibetan villages and monasteries, I met

people who know how to protect their waters. They protected the forests around the waters, and prevented livestock grazing around precious water sources. Unfortunately, many of these cultural norms have rapidly disappeared in the last 20 years.

Our legal system, which has evolved to protect private ownership regardless of its impact on living systems and human beings, must be re-examined and adjusted to protect the rights of all life.

Around the world, some governments are beginning to declare water to be a human right. Slovenia, Ecuador, Bolivia, and South Africa are leading the way in this radical idea, declaring that the earth has rights and even granting rivers personhood. India has granted legal personhood equivalent to that of a minor to the Ganges and Yamuna rivers, the Gangotri and Yamunotri glaciers, as well as a set of other natural elements. The verdicts also conferred guardianship responsibilities on city and state governments to protect these glaciers and rivers. Meanwhile, New Zealand declared in 2017 that its Whanganui River, which flows across the North Island, has the rights of personhood. This ruling reflects the tradition of the Maori, who have a saying: "We are the rivers, and the rivers are us." This ruling also designates as the river's representatives a committee from the Indigenous community that fought for these rights.[3]

"Water does not adapt to life; life adapts to water."

This movement to grant personhood for nature is one of the most effective movements, reflecting the reality of our complete dependence on water, air, and soil.

A Thousand Rivers; Ten Thousand Streams

If corporations have personhood, then surely rivers must at least have the same rights of personhood.

Trees and water are the two essential life-giving elements on earth that can interrupt climate change. Our waters have been treated as though they can be endlessly engineered, moved, and destroyed. They have become our sewers.

There are more than 84,000 dams in the United States, many of which are now in decay. Oversized hydraulic projects have interfered with the temperatures, flow, and life-giving qualities of rivers around the world. Their impact on earth's living systems is staggering.

Envision an international governance of the 1,400 major rivers and countless smaller streams and tributaries that would restore flow and aliveness to earth. We can begin a project as ambitious as the Trillion Tree Campaign. We must restore our rivers to be the primary restorative force for our ecosystems.

Let's start an international movement for rivers and streams. How can we move this into the U.N.?

Bottled Water

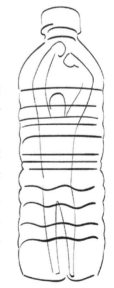

No matter what issues I raise in a lecture, the questions that I am most often asked are: What water do you drink? Which bottled water or water filter is best? What is clean water?

Here is an attempt to answer: Water is a part of everything, so the issues are not only about what you drink, but also about how your food is grown. Remember that all the food that you eat is based on water. Therefore, isn't this just as important as keeping drinking water clean?

Water's mineral content determines the taste, and also how hard or soft it is. Water from a spring can have many different minerals and will taste differently depending on those minerals. "Alive" water from a spring or well has plenty of microbes and minerals. This is the "best" water you can drink. Unfortunately, many of our springs either contain pollutants or have been destroyed. If you have a well, it is important to have the water tested annually, because various toxins can enter into our water systems. The truth is that water will always find a path, regardless of the erroneous belief perpetrated by fracking companies and other polluters that they have quarantined their dirty water somewhere safe. There are no truly impermeable boundaries.

Purified water from your drug store has been mostly emptied of healthy microbes and minerals. It is potentially less healthy to drink purified water instead of tap water, because our bodies need the naturally occurring minerals and microorganisms in order to maintain a strong immune system, and these are usually still in the tap water.

As consumers, we are confused and seduced by the word "clean." The market for bottled water is a feeding frenzy, with corporations racing to find the right combination of words to make more people buy their water. "Natural" water from springs, water that has never touched the ground, purified water, water fortified with essential minerals, locally sourced water, water from a pristine distant island, and artesian well water: all descriptions that water bottling companies have given their products to increase their appeal.

Bottled water can be useful in emergencies. However, there are large portable cleaning units which can be used to clean water after a hurricane or earthquake that eliminate the need for bottled water. Using this technology would not only cut costs, but also easily supply more people with clean water.

The Water Barons

Bottling water is an extractive industry. It sucks the water off a site, bottles it, and transports that water to faraway markets. When a bottling company moves in, a community usually loses con-

most bottled water, when tested, has been found to contain tiny pieces of plastic.

trol of its water supply. Even if the community receives an economic boost for a time, its crops, livestock, or local businesses eventually suffer. Bottled water czan not become the water that we rely on in our daily life.

In the 1980s, people began to speculate that water would eventually become "the next oil" and such a scarce a commodity that wars would be fought over it. Tragically, we're on the trajectory for this prediction to come true: water speculation is going full steam ahead, and global water speculation—the search for new markets to sell to and new sources to exploit— has become an entire industry.

In their quest to privatize resources on a massive scale,

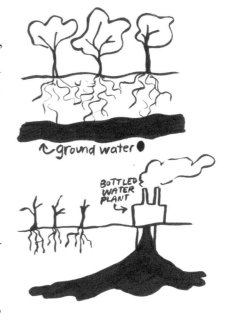

ground water

BOTTLED WATER PLANT

banks and billionaires are buying water to the extent that they are being called "water barons." Such commodification of water is no less serious as a threat to life on earth than is the fossil fuel industry. By treating water as a commodity, we evade the obligation to understand water's role in creating and sustaining all life. Many people have known that companies are buying up water, yet I was stunned to learn how extensively banks and individuals have also bought up quality water supplies around the world.

Billionaires such as T. Booke Pickens, George H. W. Bush's family, Li Ka-shing and others have bought aquifers and lakes worldwide—but because of many state regulations, individuals who have a small lake on their property cannot collect the rainwater that falls on their own property, or source water from a lake on their property. Megabanks such as Goldman Sachs, JP Morgan, Chase UBS, Deutsche Bank Credit Suisse, Macquarie Bank, Barclays Bank, the Blackstone Group, Allianz, and HSBC Bank, among others, are consolidating their control over our waters.

Speculators are predicting and creating a water crisis. Is there enough water for everyone? Is worldwide water scarcity a result of global population growth? Individuals and businesses are rushing to privatize the world's waters. Cities are running out of water, while watering their streets with drinking water. Populations are being deceived by bottled water's calculated misinformation campaigns in service of the commodification of water. We are witnessing the shortsighted drive for domination and control of our water systems, motivated by greed. Water privatization and mismanagement lack any consideration for the future of living systems or for humankind's universal dependence on those systems. Water scarcity is, by and large, the result of uninformed and incorrect decision-making: dependence

on crops unsuited for a particular area, antiquated planning, crumbling infrastructure, the use of drinking water for municipal purposes like cleaning roads and washing industrial sites, and systematic refusal to reuse and repurpose gray water (from bath tubs, showers, or washing machines) or rainwater.

Your Body is Water

"The highest form of goodness is like water.
Water knows how to benefit all things without striving with them.
It stays in places loathed by all men.
Therefore, it comes near the Tao."
—LAO TZU, TAO TEH CHING, p. 17, #8 (tr. John C. H. Wu)

One of my early curiosities was to understand how water creates patterns in the sand, carves rocks in compelling ways, and facilitates the formation of the human body.

When we are born, we are made up of about 78% water. As we age into adulthood, our bodies shift toward 50 to 60% water. Our water content declines further into old age.[4] Our hearts are 75 to 80% water, our brains 80 to 85%, and our bones 20 to 25%.

Interestingly, I found research that concludes that a healthy heart has a dynamic beat, not a regular one.[5] Water reflects our hearts: healthy water contains complex forms and minute variations, and when reduced to lifelessness, one cannot see anything but a simple pattern. Water is healthiest when it is dynamic, not stagnant or purified. The complexity of the healthy heart is paralleled by the complexity of living water.

Some time ago, I came upon an old anatomy atlas with beautiful etchings of every detail of the human body. This inspired me to make a series of visuals, called *Your Body is Water*. These images of the body reveal the flow patterns in the human body.

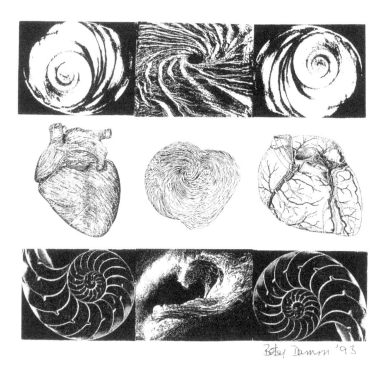

Betsy Damon '93

Like a whirlpool, the heart is a series of interlocking vortices: the most powerful self-perpetuating creative form in the universe. If you look carefully at the forms around you, you will find vortices everywhere, from leaves to galaxies.

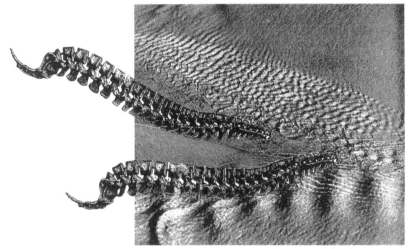

Betsy Damm '95

Spines hold up our bodies with both strength and flexibility. With its interlacing structure, a spine resembles formations made by waves passing over sand.

The muscle layer in the body and the feathers of animals share the manifold strength of streams of water, bound taut by a water molecule.

Meissner's corpuscle
(touch)

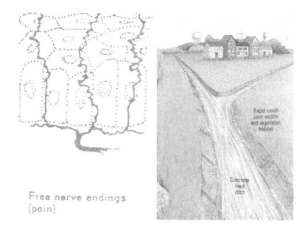

Free nerve endings
(pain)

There are infinite ways to discover how water creates form. Comparison between the skin of the earth and human skin reveals that we can scarcely tell the difference. Similarly, a healthy nervous system resembles a watershed. Compare the nerve endings of the nervous system with water systems that have been straightened into concrete ditches. Look at these nerves responding to touch, and their remarkable likeness to dynamic water systems. In the first instance, the nerves go straight and rigid in pain. Concrete ditches support only a few life forms. The relaxed nerves are sinuous and flowing. A river in connection with plants and the earth that flows freely supports complex life.

Water is the formative organizing element in our bodies. It is a tireless agent of protection, movement, and replenishment. It is our bodies' coolant in the summer and radiator in the winter. It carries and flushes waste while simultaneously bringing nutrients and oxygen to every part of us. A lack of water impacts every function in the body. In the following visuals, you'll see that the body mirrors water in many ways.

Water's Principles

To address the water crisis, we need to take a step back and understand water's most fundamental principles. The principles of water are what I think about when I am designing for and with water. For example, water was here before me. I learned from water; water did not learn from me. You might have your own ideas for principles about water—feel free to write them down. Mine are by no means absolute, rather they are my effort to reveal water.

In one water drop, there is an infinite amount of information.

Every life form on earth is created by water.

All mammal hearts are created with the vortex.

All waters are connected.

No matter how small the pipe, the water will not move in a straight line.

The natural vortex motion of water throws off pollution.

Life adapts to water, water does not adapt to life.

The primary motion of water is the vortex.

Water exists throughout the universe in perpetual motion.

My Water Story, Your Water Story

It can be nearly impossible to even consider being without water. The very act of noticing something that we depend on every minute of every day can be so overwhelming that the off switch of the brain says, "Not now." To consider water's vital role in all life and the impact on our lives is another step. We will begin to notice water together.

Each and every one of us has a water story, for we all live in a watery world. Like every human, I developed while floating protected in warm water, in the womb. I have a sense of floating in a warm, relaxing, and protected place where I was well-nourished. To this day, my body loves warm baths, hot tubs, and warm springs. My earliest memories are of sitting on the edge of the ocean, where waves gently lapped against the sand.

As I share a few stories of my relationship with water, you may begin to recall and tell your own.

When I was four, toward the end of World War II, my mother, brother, and I joined my father in Turkey, where he worked a non-army job during the war. From 1945 to 1948, we lived high in the hills outside Istanbul in a village called Rumeli Hisari. The Bosphorus, a big ribbon of salty, dark blue water that connects the

Mediterranean Sea and the Black Sea, was always in view. One could see the tides rush up toward the Black Sea and back out again to the Mediterranean. As a six-year-old, I swam in that cold, salty water on hot summer days. With nervous excitement, I avoided the barnacles clinging to the rocky shore. I loved that rocky shore, where water-carved stones, seaweed clung to rocks, and bits of shells washed up.

Colorful boats with large sails speckled the waters as they fer-ried people across from the European side to the Asian side. Perched atop chimneys, large nests built by storks dotted the skyline. The storks were considered good luck, a blessing on the home. Their wide wings swooping through the sky and over the waters became a signal that all was well.

From the hills where we lived, I could see the skyline of Istan-bul: glistening domes and tall minarets of mosques. Five times a day, calls for prayer reverberated over the hills and water and everyone from the farmers to wandering vendors lowered themselves to pray. Before entering a mosque, those who were going to pray dipped their fingers in the water. On every fountain and wall were beautifully patterned tiles.

Bosphorus from the hills

The outdoors was my play space, beneath the pine trees and wisteria arbors, or sitting among the daisies, astors, and thistles in the vast meadow just outside our garden gate. Like many young people, my cherished objects were shells, stones, nuts, feathers, flowers pressed into books. Later in life, my studio was always filled with objects that I recycled into performances and sculptures.

After each day in my one-room schoolhouse, I walked home on a small path that ran through the hills to our yard. There, climbing into a fig tree, I would swing on the supple branches and sing at the top of my lungs. From that high place, I could see the Bosphorus, and would imagine swimming across her and walking to China. In the summers, freshwater shortages left us without water for weeks. We adapted by capturing rainwater in every container, filling bathtubs, pots, and pans. I vividly remember those precious pots of water; we used only what we needed to cook with, and to wash our hands and feet.

We returned to the U.S. in 1948, first to visit my grandmother in Belmont, Massachusetts. Her property contained a natural pond where a duck family returned every year to nest. During one visit, there was a geomancer—someone practicing earth divination—walking around seeking water on her property. He handed me the V-shaped stick, encouraging me to try it out. We walked around, and as we passed over some underground water, the divining rod flew out of my hands! This experience was astonishing; my mouth dropped open as I took in this mysterious energy.

We settled near Washington, D.C. Across the street from our front yard was a stream that would swell and overflow in big rainstorms, and then recede into a trickle. In the spring, tadpoles emerged at the edges of the stream and we'd scoop them up, place them in a small container, and watch as they became frogs, before returning them to their creek. Several years later, we moved to a house built on the edge of a wooded area with a creek running in the woods behind it. "Come on, guys," I called out to my friends. "Let's dam the creek to make a small pond!" There, rolling up our pants and tossing off our shoes, we floated a poorly made raft of branches and twigs that rapidly sank under our weight.

Gathering groups to work together was second nature for me, whether it was to build a dam, or to find a way to make swings in the woods. In the summers, we would escape the Washington, D.C. heat by traveling north to my great-grandmother's home in the coastal town of Plymouth, Massachusetts. Vast woods surrounded her farm and gardens. My cousins and I swam in the salt water and roamed the beaches. We canoed in the Eel River estuaries among the cat-o-nine-tails, trying to catch turtles. We counted our time on the river with the tides, which rushed in and out. Being caught in an outbound tide would have dumped us in the ocean. Whether on the beach or in the estuaries, the tides determine the rhythm of the days. I would walk for hours, fascinated by the tidal waters, which cast up treasures and sculpted the sands.

On family trips across the United States, we drank from public water sources all along the way, and swam in water holes and streams. Today, it is unthinkable to drink from a stream or dip into a creek that you do not know. From the age of eighteen, I was privileged to be able to spend time at Squam Lake, a glacial lake at the base of New Hampshire's White Mountains. Every summer, I sat under towering pines listening to the lake and the forest humming with life. The loons' cries echoed across the waters at dawn and dusk. Diving into its cool, sweet surface refreshed me as nothing else could. I swam with loons, counted the baby ducks, and admired the old blue heron, a sentinel of the wetlands in which he fished. From a canoe, I peered at the leftovers of otters' dinners, empty shells underwater or on rocks along the shore. Big storms darkened the skies while we rushed off the lake to safety on the shore. Late in summer, mists rose in spirals every morning, shimmering as the sun bounced off the drops. In the chilly dawn, I often forced myself to climb out of my warm bed to photograph these vortices spiraling away as the sun rose higher.

Although this lake has enjoyed the protection of some conservation laws, its water quality has declined with the increase of pollutants from new developments. In particular, fire retardants entered the waters, baby loons are rarely spotted, and fewer birds sing in the early morning. I was astonished to learn that fire retardants are manufactured into everything from clothing, to new furniture to building supplies. The chemicals were entering primarily from the new housing projects where, over time, they washed out into the land and lake. These highly toxic carcinogens are used without consideration for their impact.

A seven-week camping trip across the United States with my children in the summer of 1983 would turn out to be significant in ways I never imagined. Where were the running rivers that I remembered? We encountered something unfamiliar: dry riverbeds. I knew I had never seen this on my past trips. Where were those cold streams rushing from the mountains into the lush meadows? How did so many rivers suddenly dry up? Where is the water? Those stones in the riverbeds had been washed and shaped by water for thousands of years. They reminded me of dinosaur bones found resting under a hot desert sun. At the time, I had no idea that extensive damming had dried up so many of the rivers. I imagined doing something to remind city people of the rivers that they might have forgotten, to restore their connection to their waters.

On this road trip, we unexpectedly—we were not searching for this—found our way to the first Sun Dance on the Navajo-Hopi Reservation. For four days, we witnessed the power of focused intention and prayer. We sang and drummed under a burning sun when a cloud appeared, spilling rain for five minutes out of the blue sky as the medicine man talked about the suffering of his people. The Sun Dance was a powerful, transformative experience, a specific ritual to strengthen the people and to experience suffering to gain compassion for those who are suffering. There was no separation between the dancers, the sky, the eagle, the drums, and us who chanted with them. Looking back, I realized that my vision to invite people to know about rivers originated in that experience. I cannot exactly explain how, except that it invited me to be immersed in the energies of the earth.

After returning to my loft in New York, I woke up each morning missing the trees, the simplicity of living on the earth, hearing the wind, and waking up to the dawn. This new consciousness showed up in the work that I began.

But first, to back up for a moment: Painting on canvas was my art until 1972. The sources of my new inquiries were my early morning walks with my three-year-old daughter and the feminist art movement; these worked together in not-so-obvious ways to inspire a change. I stepped out of the canvas and into public spaces with performance pieces that progressed from the personal *7000 Year Old Woman* (1976) to installations such as *Shrine for Everywoman* at UN conferences in 1980, '85, and '90.

Breathing with Stones was first performed on the streets of SoHo and then in front of the American Museum of Natural History. *Breathing with Stones* evolved into *Meditation with Stones for the Survival of the Planet* at the SOHO20 Gallery every month at the full moon. Everyone who attended an event was both healed, and a healer. Participants brought their favorite stones to a full moon performance held monthly in a SoHo gallery.

We set a large blue circular cloth in the center of the room, around which everyone stood. After a gathering of energies, a small portion of the participants were invited to lie down, heads in the center. Those standing placed stones on the bodies of those lying down on the blue circle. When finished, we intoned a vocal sound over those with the stones on their bodies. Interestingly enough, participants never told each other where to place the stones, yet inevitably they placed stones where there was tension or pain.

To complete the event, each person was invited to think about the earth: what they loved about it and what they could do to save it. We ended with an invitation to place a stone in the center of the room, while stating an intention to protect or heal something on earth. This revealed that stones are powerful vehicles for healing imbued with their own energies. The wife of the famous Nigerian drummer Babatunde Olatunji passed by the gallery and asked about the event, astonished to encounter in SoHo something she did regularly in Nigeria.

I traveled with my bags of rocks to universities and performance spaces to create these healing events. One day, the stones seemed tired, so I returned them to the earth. These stone-based performance pieces were the beginning of my exploration of the energy available to everyone, present in every detail of the earth.

In October 1983, I was invited to lead *A Meditation With Stones* at a conference in Canada for four hundred people. Many participants shed tears as they carried their rock to the center, along with a promise: "I will ensure that the whales, wolves, and bees survive." While at the conference, I met a group of papermakers who invited me to join them on a road trip to Edmonton, Canada. As we sped down the highway, I asked them, "If you could do anything, and time and money were not obstacles, what would you do?" After answering, they asked me the same question. I answered, "I can't do it, but… I imagine making a paper casting of a dry riverbed." The car came screeching to a halt at the side of the road, the people in the front seat turned around and said, "You can do that, and we will help you." At this moment, I resolved to start writing grants to secure the necessary funding. *Breathing with Stones for the Survival of the Planet* (1983) led me into water.

> "*Until one is committed, there is hesitancy, the chance to draw back, always ineffectiveness…. Whatever you can do, or dream you can, begin it. Boldness has genius, power, and magic in it.*"
> —GOETHE

Thanks to the director of the Framingham Museum, I received a new works grant from the Massachusetts Council of the Arts to create a piece for the Framingham Museum. Now I needed an accessible dry riverbed with nearby housing for up to ten people. Robyn Stein enthusiastically agreed to be the project manager. Right after returning from the UN World Conference on Women in Nairobi, we flew to Denver, rented a car, and drove through Colorado and New Mexico looking at every accessible dry riverbed. The landscape was spectacular, but suitable dry riverbeds with housing nearby were rare. Robyn's friend Lucy Wallingford recommended Castle Creek, Near Moab, Utah. Indeed, in Castle Valley, Utah, we found the perfect riverbed. Castle Creek was dry and the right size, with abundant stones carved by water.

I rented a large van and picked up the team—Coco Gordon, Robyn Stein, Denise Amses, Regina Corritore, and Helmut Becker— at the airport in Denver. With my hands trembling on the wheel, we set out and drove over the mountain and down into Moab and the 36 miles to Castle Valley. There, a local real estate man gave us a large empty house in which we slept on mats on the floor and cooked with a few pots and pans. Ray Tomasso brought his papermaking equipment from Denver. We got up early to go to the site, where Helmut began to identify the plants that would be good to gather for papermaking. Under Helmut's guidance, we pounded these plants with rocks to the rhythm of a dance. We broke down the fiber for boiling and converted it to paper. Meanwhile, the pulp had to be reconstituted by Ray. Ceremoniously, everyone lined up to support me through the first pour of the pulp onto the riverbed.

We quickly became a team, as if breathing in unison. I led the way, choosing the colors. Coco mixed the colors and for ten to twelve hours every day, Denise Amses, Regina Corritore, Robyn Stein, and Lucy Wallingford poured and patted liquid paper on every rock, bone, pebble, and bit of detritus in the dry bed. Pat

Switzer followed us with her camera. We were framed by tall red mesas and yellow poplar trees.

Memories of Clean Water

A Hopi filmmaker, Victor Masayesva, was to join us to capture the process. I had neglected to tell Victor exactly where to find us—only that we were in Castle Valley. But sure enough, he appeared one day. When I asked him how he found us, he cryptically replied, "Finding whites in the land is easy." It seemed that despite our best efforts to not disturb the land, not move a rock, and to use only biodegradable materials, none of us knew how to tread lightly on the earth.

One day, after hours of crouching over the riverbed, I stood to stretch my back and looked up. The sky was turning deep indigo and the stars of the Milky Way were beginning to appear, forming a pattern that resembled the pattern of the stones in the riverbed below. I thought, "The whole world is patterned by water, yet I know nothing about water." At this moment, I knew I had to continue along my path in learning more about water.

The next day, an elderly resident of the valley told me that the Indigenous people called the Milky Way "the river of stones." That made perfect sense and prompted me to make many large drawings of stars and stones. I was surprised to discover that nearby camping sites had signs warning people not to drink the water. Earth First!, an organization active in the area, told us that the ground and surface water was highly contaminated from mining and agriculture. In response to this shocking information, I changed the name of the piece from *A Tribute to Rivers* to *A Memory of Clean Water.*

Working so intimately in that valley with the riverbed, the stones, and the air, the mesa awakened something in me, a longing so deep that when people assumed I would go on to cast more riverbeds or other natural environments, I thought, why would I do that? Would that teach me about water?

Time Magazine covers on environment, 1988

A Memory of Clean Water became a traveling installation.* I would load the 250 feet of riverbed casting in a van and drive it around to show at museums. It sparked interest in water among viewers. It seemed that most people had not thought about where

---

* See p. 206 for a list of the participating artists and collaborators on this piece.

their water came from or went, and had never heard of aquifers or the relationships between mining and polluted waters. "Now what?" I asked myself when I returned home to New York. Although I was expected to continue casting rivers in paper, that would not have answered my questions: How does water create everything in my world? How important is water quality to life? Above all, what were the stars telling me?

The stars told me that the world is patterned by water.

Following through on my decision to know water led me to attend conferences on water. I was looking for any indication that water was more than the three stages in the hydrologic cycle, more than just wastewater to be treated, more than just a resource to be transported around and sold.

Quietly, my dad was following my work. He picked up *Sensitive Chaos: The Creation of Flowing Forms in Water and Air* at a garage sale. This book contains the research work of Theodor Schwenk, anthroposophist, engineer, and pioneering water researcher. Schwenk founded the Institute of Flow Sciences at the Max Planck Institute in Herrischried, Germany. Once I discovered Schwenk's work, I was on my way to discovering more and more about the real nature of water.

LISTENING

Listening: to give one's attention to a sound. (dictionary)

Listen *is both verb and noun*

Listening has infinite dimensions. We are always hearing the living world and rarely noticing the living world. But when we stop to listen, we notice what we are hearing. The living world is talking twenty-four hours a day, 365 days a year.

Each species has its language. Every water body, too, has its own tones: a deep silence at times, a quiet lapping against the shore, or a roaring as the winds connect with the water as it plunges, spinning in vortices racing forward. Brooks babble as they move along, some sing and some gurgle. Wetlands sing with birds, frogs, and insects, especially in the early morning and as the sun sets. A concrete ditch or a polluted wetland is often silent because so little life is in those waters.

I discovered that I could tune my heart to the ocean's waves and hear when the tides turn. My water body was connecting to its deepest origin, the ocean. Listening to water became my guide to action. Listening to each other can be the most touching, fun, connected and revolutionary act in our lives.

The Chinese character for *listen* captures the full spirit of listening. We engage our ears, eyes, and hearts to fully listen.

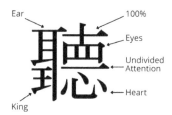

Chinese ideogram for listening (ting in Chinese)
Listening can be the most connecting and revolutionary act in our lives.

Listening is just listening, without thought, comment or interruption.

Our heads are full of thoughts, worries and distractions,
which get in the way of listening.

Equal time gives everyone room to talk.

Mistress Water

Meanwhile, I was asking myself questions. How can I avoid objectifying water? If water is not the object, then what is she? Water is the active agent in life. We know we need water. We do not say, "water did this or that," although 99% of all chemical reactions depend on water. Water is our world; we live in a watery world. She is the mistress of all life, giving birth to every detail, every part. She is the container. She is what I swim in. It is as if I were spinning around in water, yet not giving her the real power of being the container in which I am spinning.

Suddenly, water had a voice, initiative, an agency that I did not fully understand. I knew that I was part of something much larger than myself. Water was delivered to earth from space. Life evolved over eleven billion years as water cooled the surface and life slowly emerged from the sea and the mist. In 1991, I wrote:

> *Water is the foundation of life.*
> *Therefore water must be the foundation*
> *of planning and design.*

Theodor Schwenk and his colleagues at the Max Planck Water Institute explored water. They noticed that living and dead water molecules have different structures.

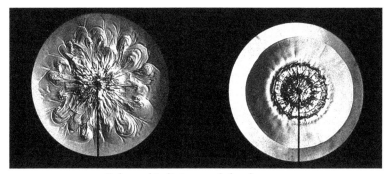

Schwenk's living and dead water

Living and Dead Water (page 40) was created by dropping a bit of water under a microscope. Healthy water contains movement created by healthy bacteria, which Schwenk's pictures reveal.

The bacteria in living water are microscopic life forms that create and sustain life. We need to keep them in our water. Humans' digestive systems benefit from the thousands of valuable microbes that water provides. Purification processes used by water utility companies remove most bacteria, the good along with the bad. On the other hand, dead water—which has been boiled or treated with chemicals—has no microbes. Distilled water isn't good for you unless a doctor has recommended it.

We live in a pulsing world. All living things pulse: trees, leaves, insects, and microbes. Each watershed, each river, has its own pulse. When a river's pulse is disrupted by dams, the life in the river is reduced. Many have witnessed that when a dam is removed, the living systems return at an astonishing rate. You can hear this change. The water moves, making the sounds of movement, and species come alive with those waters. We live and are part of all this activity. The work of Theodor Schwenk not only opened my eyes but also stimulated my curiosity: What is important about those H_2O molecules?

> *"There is no reason why scientific and spiritual research*
> *cannot come together in exploring the world we live in*
> *and the water that makes up so much of it."*
> —PAOLO CONSIGLI, *Water, Pure and Simple*

Masaru Emoto, a Japanese water researcher and scientist, has proven that water is so sensitive that its structure can respond to feelings and events.[6] This work has been disputed, yet it opened up a door into a new reality about water. What are the consequences of this kind of discovery? It is difficult to prove. We are all made up of water, and there is a direct relationship between how we feel and water's molecular structure. This relationship is natural, always there. Why are apartments with views of the water more expensive? During my later work in Beijing, I saw how the more expensive housing projects had ponds and running water features. Similarly, if you sit beside a rippling stream or stand at the ocean's edge, your body will relax. Emoto's work is one part of a larger story that is often dismissed by skeptics.

Listening in Action in Minnesota and Texas

When I go to a new place, I listen to the sounds, and to the people who live there. Listening lets us learn what is important to those who live in a particular community. They are the ones who are caring for their land and will take care of the waters. When I arrive, I try to listen with nothing on my mind except to be there.

I've worked with many people and communities to start site-specific water projects. In these workshops, we brainstormed and developed everything we could imagine: performances, exhibitions, community workshops, cleanups, lectures, and classes. The following are memorable moments among a great many attempts.

My move from New York to Minnesota in 1990 to teach art and

LISTEN TO THE PLANTS STRETCHING

activism classes at the Minneapolis College of Art and Design offered me the opportunity to work in a watery landscape. Once there, I gathered artists to begin a cleanup of a small section of the Mississippi River. Equipped with gloves and a few tools, people from age six to seventy arrived at the river. They removed trash and created sculptures along the river's edge with objects that washed up, from tree poles to roots. At the end of the day, dozens of bags of garbage had been hauled away and compelling totems stood along the riverbank, all made with a bit of twine and found wood. Everyone stayed until dark, energized by the transformation of just one mile along the river.

In Minnesota, I started by going to the headwaters of the Mississippi River in Itasca State Park. The Mississippi Headwaters bubble up through sand and tender greens in a remote meadow surrounded by ancient pines. You can feel the power of life creating in that spot. These bubbles become a mighty river; this is creation in action. I had a similar experience at the headwaters of a river near the "*God Water*," as well as at the Blue Hole outside of San Antonio—hearing, seeing, and feeling waters emerging from the earth. These places reminded me of a genesis—the beginning of a living system of arteries that sustain more life than I can imagine. I think of headwaters as being close to the beginning of something—the beginning of a drawing, writing, or any creative act that informs its evolution.

I began to learn about the waters of Minnesota by attending conferences about the Great Lakes. Speakers presented their research on the effects of chemicals on aquatic life and on those who ate fish from the lakes. The lakes were so contaminated with pollutants such as mercury and polychlorinated biphenyls (PCBs) that people, especially pregnant women, were cautioned not to eat the fish. Many people rely on fishing for their food, especially pregnant women, because healthy fish provide protein, iron, and zinc—crucial nutrients for a baby's growth and development. However, pollutants such as mercury and PCBs interfere with a baby's developing brain and nervous system.

The many factories contributing to the pollution claimed that their chemical discharge was not the cause of the contamination. But the twenty factories discharging into the same body of water created a cocktail composed of all of their released pollutants. Unfortunately, each factory wanted proof that it was "*their*" product that contributed to the pollution. And they certainly would not collectively agree to cease discharging into the lake. It was nearly impossible to call out the exact contaminant and which factory it came from. This is called *non point source pollution*, and is very difficult to address. The U.S. legal system demands that the burden of proof is on the plaintiff, which means that no factory is ever likely to take responsibility for an issue without specific proof.

I attended more conferences, in which scientists continued to report on the lakes' pollution and the impact on the fish and on humans. Scientists had spent millions of dollars studying the effects of the contaminated waters, and still no solution came forward. To the best of my knowledge, these issues have worsened. I never heard a word about the vital importance of quality water or the living system or responsibility to the community. The people most impacted were those who depend on fishing.

The Hubert Humphrey School of Public Affairs at the University of Minnesota became the home of Keepers of the Waters in 1992. Yvonne Cheek from the Hilton Head Island and I started projects in Duluth and Anoka with the help of a Jerome Foundation grant. We had no agenda except to listen. We held public meetings, focusing on concerns about water—wastewater treatment, toxic sites, and local lakes and rivers. I also started leading workshops in which everyone listened to one another's concerns, scientists gave short presentations, and the group brainstormed projects.

"Attention, for all its potent sensitivity, may be the spark that rekindles imagination." —ELLEN MELOY

The Duluth project began as a collaboration with the Pollution Control Agency and the River Watch coordinator Jill Jacoby, a creative biologist and educator. Together, we hosted a workshop for scientists to share their findings on the impact of pollutants on aquatic life in Lake Superior. Participants brainstormed projects and from this workshop, a number of public events were planned as an attempt to inform the community of Duluth about their waters. For example, an improvisational comedy troupe, Colder by the Lake, led musical events, including a radio production, while artists created exhibitions and installations outside the Duluth Museum. The idea seeped into neighboring towns, and a tourist town, Grand Marais on Lake Superior, printed water information on placemats and table signage in their restaurants.

We then visited Anoka, a small town at the confluence of the Mississippi and Rum Rivers. This confluence was once an important meeting place where traders and Indigenous peoples used the river for transportation. However, now it was considered a problematic site and maybe even a place for wastewater treatment. In Anoka, they organized a community meeting to introduce Keepers of the Waters. This meeting inspired the high school to start water programs. I was invited to teach a special art/science series focused on water and the community. We took a trip to the town's water supply, a 600-foot-deep well bore, and the source of drinking water for the city. We met the proud manager of the city water supply who had drilled the boreholes. He showed us the layers of earth through which he had drilled to reach pristine water. He voiced frustration that this pristine source of water now had to be chlorinated. There was a new national regulation that required every city with a population of more than twenty thousand to add chlorine to their water, regardless of the water's quality.

The teachers and students of Anoka learned basics about water: the ratio of fresh water on the earth, basic hydrology, how to research where their water came from, how to notice how much water they used in their house. That was enough, they were off and running.

Soon the students in the senior class were ignited with a passion to engage with their waters. They began a project in which each class taught the class below it about water. Attention to water issues grew dramatically in the town, and water became a major focal point of a large festival. When an artist painted a mural with a truck spilling chemicals on a golf course, the mayor of this small and beautiful city ordered her to remove the truck, or they would destroy the mural. Golfing was a big source of income and chemicals were always used.

If we stop to think about it, the quality of our waters has tangible effects on our everyday lives. For example, in 1983, my doctor told me not to eat celery or iceberg lettuce, explaining that because they were mostly water, they were full of fertilizers and pesticides. Everything grown in the ground will absorb the fertilizers and pest controls used. When I arrived in the Midwest in 1990, it was common knowledge that fertilizers and pesticides were contaminating groundwater. However, I was told to not mention this while teaching or lecturing, because it might offend anyone whose families were involved in the agriculture industry. In 1993, after a meeting for Keepers of the Waters at the Humphrey Institute, I overheard several professors from the agricultural school. They were talking about how if they were going to be serious about Keepers, they needed to reconsider how much fertilizer and pesticides they recommended to the farmers. Maybe by now they've begun to recommend alternatives for farmers, like crop rotation and diversity, as well as eco-friendly pesticides.

A notorious culprit in pollution is the weedkiller Roundup, which was originally produced by Monsanto, but purchased by mega-corporation Bayer in 2018. According to a University of Florida study, glyphosate—the active ingredient in Roundup—is extremely deadly for countless aquatic plants and animals.[7] This is a no-brainer; *of course,* an herbicide designed to kill plants on contact will harm any life that crosses its path. The decline in aquatic biodiversity outside America's suburbs in the past forty years should come as no surprise. Meanwhile, Monsanto has waged a targeted disinformation campaign, advertising Roundup as safe and nontoxic to human and animal life. Monsanto has faced several false advertising lawsuits, settled out of court, removed certain wording from their ads, and gone about business as usual.[8]

Even more troubling, Monsanto has exercised improper influence over studies of its herbicides. The company has also faced numerous lawsuits alleging cancer-causing effects of their product—one resulting in a two-billion-dollar settlement, which prompted Costco to pull the product from their shelves. And while several WHO and EPA studies have produced inconclusive results, internal emails from Monsanto paint a worrying picture. One Monsanto toxicologist wrote privately in 2003, "You cannot say that [our herbicide] Roundup is not a carcinogen.... We have not done the necessary testing on the formulation to make that statement. The testing on the formulations are not anywhere near the level of the active ingredient."[9] Monsanto's misinformation, propped up by unethical and incomplete science, mirrors the decades-long efforts of industries like Big Tobacco and fossil fuels to distort science for the sake of short-term profit.

However, the European Union banned Roundup, and many communities in the United States are following suit on a local level. Stores like Costco are protecting themselves from lawsuits by ditching the product. More and more people are catching on and speaking up about the damaging effects of certain chemicals used in industrial agriculture. All the same, it is not unusual for upper management to defend products that cause so much harm to both humans and nature.

In the beginning, in the Twin Cities we enjoyed a swell of enthusiasm about water, possible public projects, and action. We held a large workshop with more than sixty artists, scientists, and citizens. University of Minnesota faculty from the science, agriculture, and water management departments, as well as representatives from the Department of Parks and Recreation and other government agencies also attended. The workshop generated many ideas for remediation projects and collaborations. Parks stepped forward as a possible funder. But as suddenly as the enthusiasm began, it suddenly evaporated. St. Paul Regional Water Services contacted me to make an illustrated booklet on water uses and conservation, but their board of directors cancelled the project. Those who supervised the economic growth did not want people to know that Minnesota has lost 40% of its water quality in twenty years. My guess is that they did not want a public movement for more regulations on their lakes. Tourism and summer sports provided a high percentage of the state income. Several years after I arrived, some young people were swimming in a lake and died from the toxins in the water. One exception to this disregard for water quality was during my time with the Red Lake Band of the Chippewa people on Red Lake Reservation. They had invited me to visit, hoping that I could do something about the excessive fluoride in their waters. Alas, I did not know how to help. As I write this the situation is not much different. Edward Shu, the director of the Hubert Humphrey School at the time and a former World Bank economist, told me, "Betsy, you are ahead of your time, but you are right." He was an old guard conservative who supported Keepers, much to the confusion and surprise of his staff.

I was beginning to understand the true "aliveness" of water, and I wanted the people I'd met in Minnesota to understand it. This is when I first thought of a "living" water garden. But every time I mentioned "living" water, I was greeted with confused stares. It was as though I were speaking a secret language.

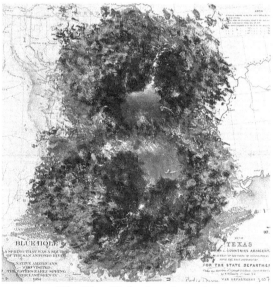

The Blue Hole, San Antonio

In 1993, I was invited to Trinity University in San Antonio to teach a class called *Art and Activism.* Upon arriving in San Antonio,

I immediately visited the Blue Hole, a sacred water site behind the Sanctuary of the Incarnate Word. There, sweet-tasting water bubbled up through a small well that formed a creek where watercresses grew, a testament to the water's high quality. This place, celebrated annually by the Indigenous Paiute people, is now dry most of the time and virtually unknown. Its existence depended on the level of water in the Edwards Aquifer, a vast body of underground tunnels formed by water boring through limestone—which is now becoming very depleted.

At the University, we were a small class of nine spirited individuals who began recycling all the Styrofoam and plastics in the dining hall and filling the halls with these objects. Off campus, we visited the Edwards Aquifer. This karst formation, a labyrinth of water-soaked porous limestone, is the source of water for most of Central Texas. Carrying bagged lunches, we ventured to the caves, where students found tons of garbage, plastics, and metals. These explorations became fodder for performances and sculptures. The San Antonio Riverwalk, a mile-long walkway through commercial enterprises, is a famous attraction that consists of a leftover bit of river, after the river was rerouted around the city. One student found the neglected park beside the real river, and decided that her final project would be a cleanup of the park. Her event became the first of what is now an annual cleanup of the San Antonio River. The professors of the art department were not pleased with all these trashy pieces and events. They did not think any of this was "real art," or that it required the skills that they'd taught.

While in San Antonio, a newly formed citizens' group invited me to their meetings. They were addressing issues of the Edwards Aquifer where developers were constantly trying to encroach on this fragile system. The group claims that our potluck evenings inspired them to start Save the Edwards Aquifer. Now, this aquifer is federally protected, but, even so, it is still being depleted by unchecked real estate development.

Swede Hollow and Phalen Creek

After a few months in San Antonio, I was back up to St. Paul, Minnesota, and in an artists' loft beside the Mississippi River. Nearby was Swede Hollow, at that time considered a free dump. About two hundred years ago, Swede Hollow was the perfect wintering ground for Indigenous people. The valley provided protection from winter weather and contained multiple springs that fed Phalen Creek, which flowed into a large estuary and the Mississippi River. After Edward Phalen arrived in 1841, settlers began to pour in, forcing the Indigenous people out and eventually demolishing their sacred cave in the cliffs above the entrance to Swede Hollow and overlooking the river. This cave was once a place of ceremony for the tribes. After the railroad was built along the banks of the Mississippi, people hopped off the train, and those who were penniless squatted in the hollow for the winter. By the time we discovered it, the hollow had become a garbage dump surrounded by many deteriorating and abandoned houses. During our visits to this place, we noticed a lone man removing old tires and trash from the pond. Some of us decided to join in his efforts. We started meeting at a local café on the edge of the creek and began organizing cleanups. Christine Baeumler, who was part of the early effort, later created *Henge*, a piece formed from remnants of buildings and stones found on the site. Her work focused further attention on the possibilities of this deep ravine and its waters.

After this, the upstream portions of Phalen Creek were daylighted and reconnected to the pond in the hollow. Now, twenty years later, the entire system is planned to reconnect to the Mississippi River and the hollow is an urban wildlife refuge and park. Artists had begun and moved the project along. Thirty years ago, the head of the St. Paul parks department told me that there was "no such thing as a natural river," and that they would never reconnect Phalen Creek to the Mississippi. To my shock, it was the parks department that just put the creek into pipes rather than build a bridge over it.

Mississippi River Cleanup

To start a project, it is essential to listen to people. I learn what they care about, what they know, and about their jobs, skills, limitations, discouragements, and hopes. In every location, the people who live there are those who care for their waters. The projects that they choose to do are theirs, not mine.

These are a few examples of success stories. But when I look back on those years, I see a long trail of *starts*, some of which have evolved into larger initiatives. These starts were often modest, but many laid the groundwork for the future. You never know what will happen if you initiate a conversation and invite people to act. We face walls like intimidating power structures and confusing bureaucracy, misinformation and confusion. But it is often the *internal* walls that discourage us the most: the voice inside our heads telling us that our efforts would be useless. One thing was clear: artists can start without needing to ask, "Can I clean this up? Can I make something out of this junk?"

Listening is different from hearing. Most of the time hearing goes in one ear and out the other. Too often I have participated in what I call fake listening. A landscape company or city planning agency will call a meeting to "listen" to a community to find out what the community wants. They do this either to fulfill a requirement, or to stave off community pushback on their plan. Then they collect—or pretend to collect—the community's ideas for the business to be able to get the funding they wanted.

Fake listening is what happens too often when an initiating body wants certain answers. They listen for what they want and create questions that address their own concerns and not necessarily the concerns of those attending. How can we create a space for real listening in which each person can find themselves? The underlying question for each person was: *What is a meaningful action that I can begin?* Hearing, on the other hand, tends to go in one ear and out of the other.

Despite all these projects, I faced a big wall of discouragement. Real water projects required more funding than an artist alone could receive, and the local, state, and national control of water seemed impossible to penetrate. Few wanted the public to become knowledgeable and empowered about their water systems. There was a great deal more resistance than acceptance, and the resistance came from those in control, ranging from corporate interests to utility companies. Projects engaging with water—save those in your backyard or private land—require collaboration and support.

Listening deeply is the primary initiating action. Once people experience really being heard, they themselves can begin to listen and consider new ideas. Listening enables every person—no matter their culture, education, gender, age, or race—to find their own thinking. Choose to connect with and listen to people you don't know. Listening is also the best skill to make a community meeting go smoothly. In a group, it's important to find a way for people to have approximately equal time to speak. Equal time gives space and encouragement to people who are not accustomed to speaking in a group, while allowing equal space for those who *are* accustomed to speaking. Often people are just waiting to be asked, and enjoy sharing their thinking and knowledge when they're given the chance to do so.

THE ARTS

The primary movement that I am in is the flow of waters.

"The sage's transformation of the world
arises from solving the problem of water."
—LAO TZE, Chinese sage, sixth century BC

Curiosity propels me forward. Creativity is an ever-flexible, expansive process available to everyone—not only all humans, but also the entire living universe. Chaos and change are opportunities. How does that H_2O molecule create such a vast and impressive complexity of life? How does it support the living systems upon which we all depend? Collaboration with the living world brings forth pathways for discovery. As one step finishes, the next one appears. The feminist movement invited me into myself, into listening intensely to myself and to others. *Breathing with Stones for the Survival of the Planet* revealed what I knew as a child—that the living world has agency, is animated.

In the words of Gilah Yelin Hirsch, of the International Society for the Study of Subtle Energies and Energy Medicine:

Humankind is gifted with a deep well of imagination waiting to be tapped. Times of adversity can stimulate creativity to voyage beyond immediacy. Original innovation flourishes in unpredictability and that which has not yet been found. Ideas and images are mined in uncertainty and unknowing. Every event can be perceived as an opportunity to uniquely and positively mirror the moment with new perspective.

Micro and Macro Universe

The Heartbeat of a Society

The arts are the heartbeat of a society—they are the wonderful hum of people doing, documenting, articulating, inventing, celebrating. Art enables our minds to envision changing things that seem immutable. More often than we know it is the artist who envisions that change first, and then expresses their vision for change. Leonardo da Vinci imagined a flying machine. One artist jumped the fence around the Los Angeles River and planted a tree. Another created a forest as his art piece. And these initiatives number in the thousands. These are actions and works that cannot be bought or sold. And although the works sometimes rapidly disappear, the actions behind them have led to more and more like them. Now the Los Angeles River is being restored, and Swede Hollow is a notable ecosystem.

Where do artists belong? Artists belong everywhere, and *are* everywhere. They are in the streets, coffee shops, kitchens, back rooms, and in both private and public spaces.

Thousands of artists have turned their attention to the earth, to the waters, plants, and animals, and to climate change. Their work has educated, inspired, initiated projects, and started major changes. Artists and scientists are coming together to create solutions and inspire innovations. They are standing up, creating new possibilities, and are inviting many to notice the world in which we live.

> *"In Indigenous culture, there's no separation*
> *between art and life."* —JOHN LOPEZ

Artists are the people who create vision and hope, who inspire change. The list of eco-artists working around the world is long, and I wish I could name and honor every one of them. They often work invisibly in the center of their communities. No monetary value can begin to describe the contributions of those who have dedicated themselves to making the world a better place for life to thrive.

Throughout time, humans have created: a cutting instrument, a chopstick, the wheel, paintings and carvings on all kinds of surfaces, airplanes and rockets, computers and movies, and now a worldwide network of communications. Creativity is that dynamically alive pulse in a world governed by the pulse of waters.

Past Dreams and Future Visions: Chengdu and Lhasa

While I was teaching and working in the Twin Cities, China began to come into focus, fulfilling a childhood fantasy of mine. As a child, I sat at my great-grandmother's feet in her living room overlooking the Atlantic Ocean in Plymouth, Massachusetts. She told me stories of her grandfather, a sea captain. Her home was full of Chinese art. During a year in Japan in 1960, I participated in a dig at a five-thousand-year-old archaeological site, with a professor named Dr. James Kidder. I spent two days a week learning Japanese calligraphy and I studied the history and art of China, Japan, and Korea. However, it was my son, Jon, who was learning Chinese in high school, who initiated this later trip to China. My two children, Tamara and Jon, and I planned a trip for May 1989. I decided to follow through with our plans, even though the Tiananmen Square protests were happening. Our jumbo jet contained only seven passengers. Landing in Beijing, we looked down and saw bonfires in the streets. We explored the city on rented bikes. However Tiananmen Square was a magnet, and we spent many hours talking with demonstrators there. After four days, we had to proceed with our planned schedule to go to Chengdu, Sichuan.

There, we found another world. Chengdu is an ancient city, four thousand years old, full of street life, a Tang dynasty cultural center. Our hotel was on a large central street where a huge student demonstration was happening at the foot of the Mao sculpture. The China International Travel Service Corporation (CITS) made sure that we were tourists for three days before resuming our schedule and flying to Kunming. In Kunming, everything had stopped. We were able to abandon our schedule and find our way by bus into a remote area where early one morning on a public loudspeaker we learned about the violent ending of the student sit-in. Heartbroken, we returned to Kunming and were flown to Hong Kong. Jon had fallen in love with China and decided that he wanted to return as a student at Peking University in Beijing.

In the summer of 1991, Tamara and I joined Jon in Chengdu. While we were dragging ourselves along an avenue in the July heat, a woman tapped me on the shoulder. She asked if we could spend the day speaking English with a group of Chinese professors who were learning English. Eagerly, we all said yes. After a day with the professors, while eating dinner, I fell into a conversation with a biologist. He was studying whether a certain water source had real health benefits. This pristine water, known as the "*God* Water," was from a site twenty hours to the north. He had found that the waters reduced tumors in mice and assisted with digestion. My curiosity was piqued. I told him I would love to see the place. He replied, "No, you wouldn't. It's hard to get to, and it's just a muddy hole." Regardless, I silently resolved to visit the *God* Water.

With a travel grant from the Jerome Foundation, I went back to Chengdu in 1993. My son Jon, who after a year at Peking University, was now quite fluent in Chinese and agreed to come with me. With only an address scratched on paper, we began searching for the owners of a water bottling company that sourced from the God Water. We found a tiny office on a back street in Chengdu. Their shock at the two foreigners walking into their office was palpable; they immediately offered to drive us to their bottling facility. A few days later, in an old army jeep with no shocks, we started on the nineteen-hour trip. Jon, who is over six feet tall, squeezed into the back seat, his groans audible as we bounced along the terrible roads. Finally, we stopped overnight at an inn. There, huddled on small wooden stools, hands held out around the charcoal burner, I said to our guides, who were the owners of this factory, "I bet that you were good young Red Guards." They enthusiastically replied that they were; it had changed their lives, and now they are starting this business.

The next morning, the developed world slipped from view as we climbed through high meadows and forests up steep, rutted dirt roads carved into the side of a mountain. There, buried in an old-growth forest, was a small wooden factory situated above

Site of the God Water

The God Water

the *God* Water. The owners of the factory and the local officials welcomed us with a many-course meal spread out on tables under the towering pines. We were the first foreigners to visit this place. Our hosts pointed out that their wooden factory was eco-friendly. After lunch, we wound down a ravine, through ferns, rhododendron, and moss-covered rocks to a small new pagoda marking the place of a spring. The one discordant note was a barbed wire fence that surrounded the site.

With a ceremonial dipper, we were offered a drink of the water. Immediately after drinking, my body responded with sensations that I had never experienced before. I felt an inexplicable aliveness throughout my body, on a seemingly cellular level. The wall of discouragement buried deep inside of me dissipated. I thought, "I cannot give up my work with water."

That night, I slept in a simple room. My head was spinning with new knowledge. I thought about what happens when a community-sustaining water source is bottled and sent far away. The water is dislocated, becomes anonymous, and the people who have protected and relied upon this water for thousands of years are cut off from their life source. I was discovering that pristine well waters were once the sustaining heart of a community. That was exactly my experience in the Twin Cities. When I first arrived in the Twin Cities in 1990, there were artesian wells where people lined up with glass jugs to pump the water. When I asked them why, they responded by saying things like "my wife is healthier with this water" or "my coffee tastes better with this water." Within one or two generations, the rich history and quality of life supported by these waters vanished. Something much larger was lost.

At the *God* Water, the locals were now forbidden to source their water at the spring and were cutting the barbed wire to get down to it. As a concession, the factory owners installed a small pipe leading from the spring up the steep ravine to a trash heap of broken glass behind the factory. The factory owners claimed that this pipe was an improvement; people no longer had to pay a lama who diagnosed the illness and then wrote how much water to drink. We learned that because glass bottles filled with water were too heavy to transport down the mountain, they had to switch to plastic bottles—only to discover that the water, when stored in plastic, lost its medicinal properties within a few days.

Visiting this site was not unlike choosing to cast a dry riverbed. It propelled me forward toward new possibilities by providing me with an instant and visceral understanding of the importance of living water, as well as how this importance was being forgotten. This water was protected by villagers for over 1,500 years. It was carefully regulated and was used only to heal. For a small fee, a lama would prescribe how much water someone should drink to cure their illness.

Lying there listening to the birds, I knew that there was a vast difference between knowing and respecting water, and bottling and selling water. After two days in the mountains, we set off. Little did I know how much my life was about to change. The waters took charge, clearing a path for me as I dedicated myself clearly to them.

While hanging out in Chengdu preparing to visit the *God* Water, I was asked if I wanted to attend a conference on the environment. This conference, serendipitously, was to occur right after my trip to the *God* Water and included Chinese engineers and Qigong Masters, a group from Japan, and Europeans who were studying Qigong. This was the first conference created by the Chinese, for the Chinese.

At the conference, I spoke about my activist work in Minnesota. The idea of activism aroused visible excitement among older Chinese scholars and engineers, who agreed that this would be great to do in China. I learned fascinating things from them, such as that the water found inside of bamboo is the best for your heart. They spoke about identifying good water, and the effects of that water on the body. This meeting was the first that reassured me that my preoccupation with the importance of quality water was completely rational.

After listening to them, I could fully imagine the Living Water Garden that I had been talking about in Minnesota.

Quickly we brainstormed a project that we called *Living Yangtze*. They could envision it! The project was designed to have people from both Chinese and American cities team up on the Yangtze and Mississippi Rivers, and exchange information about how to keep those rivers clean. Downstream, rather than being a waste stream, there would be a clean stream.

Returning to the United States with renewed optimism, I began to apply for grants only to discover that no one would fund work in China. Interestingly, I was approached by a headhunter for the Dayton Foundation to lead a downstream project on the Mississippi River before going to China. During the interview, I proposed a collaborative downstream project for the Mississippi River in which the towns on the river would gather their citizens, farmers, industrialists, and others to discuss how they could start to clean the river. His response was to accuse me of being a communist. But what other way could it ever be possible to clean up the river and address the multiple sources of pollution?

Again, I found myself trying to find a way through or around these irrational walls. Out of the blue, a woman called me and said, "I want to fund you." She did not explain who she was, or what she was considering. Spontaneously, I found myself telling her about the *Living Yangtze* vision. She gave me more than half of the funding necessary to initiate an artist-run public education project on a river in China. Most of my friends tried to talk me out of going to China. "Impossible," they said. Nonetheless, some helped me raise another ten thousand dollars, and I began to prepare to return to Chengdu. In 1995, without an official invitation from a registered Chinese institution, only tourists could enter the country. On top of that, after the protests in Tiananmen Square in 1989, the government had banned all public art, so I knew that I would never get an official invitation to create public art for water.

I went to Chengdu with twenty-four thousand dollars in a money belt, and no formal invitation from the Chinese. Kristin Caskey, an MFA student, joined me as an assistant. With tourist visas, we started our trip in Hong Kong and found a way to cross over into China and flew to Chengdu.

With only one phone number saved from the conference two years ago—that of Dr. Zhu Xiao Feng of the Academy of Social Science—we went to our hotel. I had sent him messages that we would be coming, but I never heard back. On day six, Dr. Zhu Xiao Feng appeared at our hotel; he had been searching for us, too.

We booked rooms at the foreign guesthouse in the West China University of Medical Sciences and began meeting people that Xiao Feng introduced us to. One was Li Shao Lin, the new Head of Water Quality for the city. She recruited Zhang Xuehua, her niece who spoke English, to assist me. In trying to understand what my ideas and motives were, she repeatedly asked, "What is it that you *really* want to do?" Apparently, activist art was a mystery, and a foreign woman who wanted to make art on and about a river was an even greater mystery. I found myself talking with small but highly attentive groups of people in the park. One person who came was an artist named Dai Guangyu, who would become a key organizer in the following months. Each person I met was nervous, but curious.

To begin, Zhu Xiao Feng, Zhang Xuehua, Kristin Caskey and I went to a small, historic town at the confluence of two rivers to explore if this would be a good place for the events. It was good to leave the city and sit beside a flowing river, under a large tree, drinking tea and discussing what we could do. We dreamed of who we were in the Tang Dynasty, 617 to 907, the golden age of China. Chengdu was a cultural center, with beautifully constructed brick cisterns that were used to deliver clean water to the city and remove polluted water. These water systems were being discovered as developers dug the foundations for new buildings. Late at night, we would go to view them while devoted archaeologists were collecting the remains to reconstruct them for museums.

Meeting under a tree

Finding the headwaters of a river is a bit of an obsession for me. After three weeks of organizing, it was time to fulfill a lifelong dream, setting out for the headwaters of the Yangtze River. The difficult trip started in Golmud, a desolate mining town at nine thousand feet above sea level. Zhu Xiao Feng, Kristen Caskey, Jon and I piled into two jeeps with two guides and all the equipment. After three long days on dusty roads, we arrived at a small Tibetan village and left the road for three more days of traversing the glacial moraine. On the afternoon of the third day, we rounded a corner to see in the distance a huge glacier—the source of the Yangtze. This was Mother Earth writ large, spilling her waters from inside, endlessly pouring forth an awe-inspiring bounty. This was the miracle of life beginning. Flashing through my mind was the distance this river flows—3,915 miles to Shanghai. What is happening to the life downstream, where these amazing waters are overwhelmed with pollution? It is said that not long ago every spring a group of Tibetans would visit the headwaters to honor them with prayers

In a short two days, we were back in the small village sitting in a warm room, hands wrapped around teacups, staring back at the young Tibetan men who stared at us. Xiao Feng suggested that we go to Lhasa, the mythic capital of Tibet. All the buses were full, so Xiao Feng found a truck driver who was willing to drive us to Lhasa. With legs shaking, I boarded the truck and we began our ascent up the highest pass in the world. All of this was highly illegal. If we were caught, the punishments would be bad.

Yangtze headwaters

While recovering at a Tibetan hotel, I said, "Let's meet artists." Most of them could be found in galleries that were at the time located in the Potala, the old palace of the Dalai Lama that dominates the skyline. Four of the artists we met decided to join us in Chengdu.

An airplane was the only fast option to return to Chengdu. Soon, we were settling into the guesthouse of the West China Medical

Chengdu middle schoolers looking into river

Center of Sichuan University. Jill Jacoby and biologist Ann Middleton flew in from the U.S., bringing water test kits and nets. I began my day biking along the river each morning, accompanied by butterflies sitting on my handlebars. There is nothing like the mystery of word of mouth in China: soon artists from Beijing, Shanghai, Lhasa, and the U.S. arrived to join the Chengdu group. There were three major hurdles to the project. First, we had no official sponsor, so legally speaking, we couldn't do anything except be tourists. Second, we had no place to meet. Third, we faced significant cultural and language barriers. Fortunately, translators from the West China Medical Center eagerly joined us.

The first step was to get to know the river. We learned about the fifty-four fish species that had disappeared in the past thirty years. We studied Sichuan's four major historical water projects. In the first project, water runoff from a mountain was diverted to flow in two directions instead of one. The second project was the Dujiangyan Irrigation System in 256 BC. Still working today, this project is an incredible example of naturally distributing the water of the Ming River across an agricultural plane. The third and fourth projects both addressed flood control and the connection of the Jian River of Chengdu. The current project would restore the flood control of the Fu-Nan River and create the Emerald Necklace, a system of parks along the rivers.

We walked down old stone steps carved by thousands of human feet, noticing the dark slime of sewage that was present. We learned from listening to the elders who knew this river from a time, not long ago, when they caught their dinner in it and dived into the water for a swim or bath. Still, after every rain, people would stand on the

Ancient method of fishing

edge of the river, fishing with large nets and hoping to catch a few small fish washed downstream by the fresh water. Each artist's mind was searching for creative ways to direct attention to this river. We began weekly meetings, picnics, and dinners to discuss what we would do on Chengdu's Fu-nan River.

Eventually the Chengdu Environmental Protection Agency gave us space. I was mystified that at our meetings, no one would talk with people whom they did not know. Awkwardly, we started to break this barrier. I asked the group why they didn't look at each other or say "hello" when they entered the room. I decided to demonstrate a big "hello" with a hug. Everyone wanted to hug this foreign woman, and laughing through it all, we hugged and hugged. My son Jon asked, "What about me?" and giggling girls went rushing into his arms. From then on, many people ate together. Everyone went on picnics and adventures. The group began forming a collective process among themselves. Well aware that someone was always observing us, we were able to show that there was nothing subversive happening.

In the weekly meetings, everyone brainstormed and shared ideas. We all lived simply on five dollars a day. The artists had to decide among themselves how to use the seven thousand dollars for projects. If an idea took up too much of the budget, they assisted each other in coming to a better decision. The collaboration appeared to be easy and seamless.

Receiving permission from the government was our largest obstacle. Each artist was required by the government to submit their ideas with titles. When we didn't hear anything encouraging from the government, we prepared to go to a small place in the countryside to create the work and document what happened.

At the end of July and in the middle of this process, I was invited to see the Chengdu city government plans for the whole river. A black government car picked me up to take me to meet with a group on the sidewalk in front of an old pagoda. There, I looked at plans for restoring the river. I praised the plans that called for a ring of parks on both sides of the river—there was no economic development such as entertainment, restaurants or waterside apartment buildings. Their plan was to restore the river and make an "Emerald Necklace" through the city. I questioned them about the design for flood control, knowing that floodwalls were not the answer. The chief engineer told me that this is how it was done on the Los Angeles River. I learned that the manual for flood control used in China since 1942 was the U.S. Army Corps of Engineers manual.

Then I asked, "Why don't you make a park to teach people how nature can clean water?" Without hesitation, they asked, "Can you do that?" I nodded silently. Following more discussion between them, they said, "We want you to do that, and not those performances." I suspect that they did not know the content of the performances and were acting protectively because public art had been forbidden since Tiananmen. I told them I would think about it. The next morning, after a sleepless night, I told them that we needed to complete the work that I was given the funding to do. The government responded by saying that they thought performance art was a waste of time and money, but that they would watch me carefully. If they liked what happened, they would invite me back to design the park.

Just when we were about to give up and go into the countryside, suddenly we got permission. Everything brightened, as if a big dark cloud had lifted from Chengdu. The citizens, students, and businesses all pitched in to help with the events. Over a two-week period, in August of 1995, instal-

Start of the two weeks of water protection

lations and performances animated the banks of the river between two prominent bridges.

The events began with a small parade to the river holding a banner that read *Keepers of the Waters* in Chinese and English. Sculptures and performances invited the public to the river. Some pieces were interactive and others invited dialogue.*

We began with *Washing Silk*: six women wearing red gloves stood in the river holding long white pieces of silk, which rapidly turned dark gray. Another piece, *Washing River*, by Yin Xiuzhen (尹秀珍), involved freezing polluted water into ice blocks to make a four-foot square, which people scrubbed with brushes. As the ice blocks melted, poets recited their texts, the conversation grew, and the spirit of the city started to emerge. In one piece by Liu Chengying (劉成英), titled *When Will Fun-Nan River Have Fish and Shrimp— Calling of Ducks*, 21 ducks swam in pens, wearing signs around their necks. *Long-Abandoned Water Standards* by Dai Guangyu (戴光郁) included a large billboard full of information about the river, while beneath it photos of all our faces in small pans were being eaten away by the river water. Other pieces included sculptures of old men fishing on dry land, as well as washing stands with basins inviting people to wash using the river water.

The two-week project was featured on Chinese TV every day. The art activities brought attention to the waters, invited public awareness, and inspired something intangible: hope.

In the final event, *Dreams for a Pure River* by Christine Baeumler and Beth Grossman, people told stories and placed their dreams with lotus flowers on a raft of bamboo. We lit candles on the rafts and sent them downstream while people ran after them along the riverbank. Everyone watched until the last candles flickered out. The stories were transcribed and presented to the Environmental Protection Agency of Chengdu. The raft was retrieved and the materials in it were given away, so that the next morning what was left was "the memory of everyone coming together to celebrate their precious river and plan to restore it to its glory."[10]

---

* For a partial list of participating artists and facilitators see p. 205.

Washing Silk *by Ang Sang* (昂桑), *Ge Ci* (格次), *He Qichao* (何啟超),
Kristin Caskey, Suri Lamnu (次仁拉姆), *Tang Liping* (唐利平),
Yu Leiqing (俞雷慶), *Zhou Zheng* (周正)

Washing River *by Yin Xiuzhen* (尹秀珍)

The Water Propaganda Board *by Dai Guangyu* (戴光郁).
A high official signed this board, publicly indicating his support.

Dreams for a Pure River *by Christine Baeumler and Beth Grossman*

During these events, news reporters thrust microphones in front of me, asking: *Why Chengdu? How did you get here?* I was asked these questions over and over because very few foreigners ever found their way inland to Chengdu. I replied that I was trying to find a way to get people involved with their waters. The events were broadcast on the national television station, CCTV, throughout the two weeks of the project. Though I called these projects *Keepers of the Waters Chengdu,* the government renamed the project *A Week of Water Protection.*

The Living Water Garden

The spirit of these public events in Chengdu was contagious—the government wanted the ideas, the spirit, to remain in the city. I would be invited back to design the first urban park designed as a water cleaning system.

Back in the U.S., I searched for a landscape architect who understood "living" systems design—incorporating natural processes of regeneration into design. I found Margie Ruddick. I wrote grants to be able to return to China, but was rejected because China was a communist country, or—as one potential funder said—the Chinese would never do a project like this; they were "liars." Frustrated, I put the airfare on a charge card and returned to China.

Back in Chengdu, I was joined by Margie Ruddick and my son Jon. We were put up at a new complex that served as the headquarters of the river restoration construction group. To begin, a large meeting was called. We entered the room where more than forty people sat around a long table ceremoniously decorated with flowers surrounding Chinese flags. I sat beside a dean from Sichuan University, whom I had met the previous summer. He smiled gently and said, "Don't be nervous, you have friends here."

Calming myself, I presented the concept of a living water garden, a park that shows how nature cleans water. Two years later, Zhang Jihai, the director of the Five Year Plan, told me that after he heard me talk about this park, he was very excited and resolved to give his full support to the project. Following a lively discussion, we all ate lunch, then were taken by bus to look at possible sites. We were informed that within a week, we would know which site had been chosen. A week passed, and true to their word, the government officials told us, "We are giving you the largest inner-city park along the river." They asked me which people I needed on the team, and I requested a bioengineer and a landscape designer. Miraculously, the only bioengineer in Western China was there. His name was Huang Shida, a hydraulic engineer from Sichuan University. He was visibly excited by the idea of cleaning with plants, and knew exactly what the system would need. He set about pouring river water into concrete bins to figure out exactly which plant species needed to be included. We were introduced to the landscape design company that had designed other parks on the river. Clearly they were not happy with the decision to give their already-designed park area over to the Living Water Garden.

There are many fascinating details connected to this exceptional journey to create a park that demonstrates how nature cleans water. To begin the three weeks, Margie Ruddick and I walked the park often, trying to imagine what it would look like. Huang Shida shared with us the function of each of the seven stages in the cleaning system. We established a high point, from which all the water pumped into a settling pond would flow through the plant-cleaning ponds, into a pond with fish, and finally to the clean-water area. All the waters flowed by gravity. Within two months, we had enough of the plan to make a large model, which was displayed in a public building nearby. Over the next five months, the model was carried from neighborhood to neighborhood, where retired elders volunteered to present the concept to the public.

The design used only one pump. The most notable aspect of the project is that it is a completely interconnected system. Each section is dependent on the section before it, making the Living Water Garden a complex and resilient place that has survived many abuses. When the systems are connected, the pollution cannot build up and the plants survive despite neglect.

After three months, we had done all that we could, but did not yet know if the park would be approved, so we returned to the US to wait for the news.

After receiving a Bush Foundation individual artist grant for my public art practice and community activism with water, I decided to go to Lhasa in August of 1996, at the invitation of the Tibetan artists. Given the long history of conflict between China and Tibet, tensions were high. Nevertheless, we went, along with two translators and Suvan Geer, an installation artist from Los Angeles. Once again, Zhu Xiao Feng started organizing. As word spread, many other Chinese artists piled in.

Our meetings were held in the rooftop café of one of the Tibetan hotels. The politics were complex and difficult. The Tibetans sent delegates to our meetings. Open discussions about ideas and costs were difficult, because the Tibetans were so reluctant to disclose what they might create. Again we had to submit all the ideas to the government for approval.

After two weeks of planning, we held three days of events and performances along the Lhasa River and in the National People's

Park behind the Potala Palace. One artist initiated a prayer procession along the riverbank, which could be seen in the background of a television newscast in which an official spoke on the scene. Again the work of many artists animated the riverbank and the Potala Garden. Yin Xiuzhen worked with a school and brought along dozens of boys dressed in their best clothes to fly kites. Unfortunately, the wind was too weak that day, so the boys ended up hanging bags of water on chopsticks at the water's edge. Many of the installations were stunning and innovative. As I suspected, the Tibetan artists created impressive works. In a closing event, the Tibetan artists hung T-shirts on poles planted in the shallow waters, claiming the river with ghosts of their ancestors. We ended the experience with a feast of roasted lamb by the river.

After our time in Lhasa, five of us traveled to Lake Namtso, the highest saltwater lake in the world. Lake Namtso is a pilgrimage site. A small group of monks lives in a cave overlooking its shores. On the first day, I wandered to the shores of the lake and listened to the lapping of the waves. I heard them saying, "You know what to do, go do it." I still often wonder what the lake was inviting me to do. The next morning, one of us woke up unable to move. With the help of the other two, I calmed her down and was able to adjust her spine enough for her to walk.

Back in Chengdu, the Living Water Garden was stuck in an internal process, which excluded us; so we returned to the U.S. Then suddenly, in late January 1997, I got a telegram that they were starting the construction of the park. How was this possible? The design had not been completed; it was only in concept, not in detail. It's important to understand that I had little real control here. The government hired everyone who worked on the park. The construction documents were inadequate. Details were missing. In February 1997, I was on my way back to Chengdu, stopping again in the Netherlands to see some living water systems.

Sweeping River *by Zhang Shengquan (張盛泉)*

Stamping the Water *by Song Dong (宋冬)*

Living Water *by Yin Xiuzhen (尹秀珍)*

Tibetans Take Back the River *by Ang Sang (昂桑), Ang Xin, Dai Guangyu (戴光郁), Li Jixiang (李繼祥), Liu Chengying (劉成英), Ruan Haiying (阮海鷹), Song Dong (宋冬), Suri Lamnu (次仁拉姆), Suvan Geer, Yang Kayva, Yin Xiuzhen (尹秀珍), Zhang Lei (張蕾), Zhang Shengquan (張盛泉), Zhang Xin (張新)*

Coincidentally, I had met a woman the previous year in the courtyard of the Foreign Experts housing in the University who knew the Director of Water Infrastructure for the Netherlands. He took me to various sites that were already adapted to the rising waters. At one site, three different water systems funneled dirty water from the top of a hill into large containers at the bottom. One of the systems was a traditional step system, and the other two were created with flowforms that moved water in a figure-eight, vortex motion. The same amount of dissolved oxygen was measured at the end of each of the three, but in the receiving bins of the two flowform systems, complex floral vegetation grew—and nothing was thriving in the waters from the step system. This revealed that the bio-dynamism of the waters moving in a vortex motion was greater than in the waters that poured over steps, and made an as yet unmeasurable but significant difference.

I left Amsterdam to meet Jon in Chengdu. Jon could barely contain his excitement that construction had started. Immediately we hurried to visit the site of the Living Water Garden. There was a huge hole in the middle of the construction site. I thought, "What's that big hole doing there?" We walked down into the hole to speak with a portly man who was the head of a construction company. He told us that he was building a parking garage. Apparently, the government had added this to the plans, probably as some sort of condition for the project to be allowed to happen. I said, "I hope the roof is strong enough to hold a water system!" Puffing up his chest, he assured me that it would be. Given this new and surprising element, we had to immediately redesign many aspects of the park. Although my intention was to complete the design and leave, I stayed for the next nine months to complete the designs on the run. Every week, the designs were corrected in a large meeting. The blueprints were inadequate because no one knew how to design to the level of detail necessary. They soon discovered that the roof of the parking garage wasn't strong enough to support a constructed wetland. A new roof cost us three feet of the well-calculated slope. I have no idea what this mistake cost the government. I do know what this mistake cost the design.

Flowforms are designed for a specific slope and length. These forms invite water to oscillate in a vortex motion. They transfer water from one section to another, increasing the motion of the dirty water molecules not only to oxygenate the water but also to increase the water's vibration for life. Because of interference from the parking garage, the flowforms had to be reduced in height by three feet. Nevertheless, the flowforms are still the most fascinating and informative feature in the park for young visitors. Fish gather in the pond where the flowforms deposit the waters.

Huang Shida, the hydraulic engineer, camped out with his team of students in an apartment overlooking the park for the year, as he directed the building and planting of the wetlands.

I spent much of my time sculpting the central fountain, the three flowform systems, and the chambered nautilus piece with the help of a sculptor named Denglu. Jon was tracking it all in addition to participating in various internal negotiations over what kind of toilet to use, how to fix this or that. The Chinese landscape design company quietly discarded many of my designs in favor of their own, but their designs eventually had to be replaced because they were not functional with a water system. We were often part of collective processes that lasted as long as necessary for everyone to reach an agreement. Those opposed to the park had an undeclared strategy to attack us to protect themselves, and then after a lengthy process agreed to go forward. My team always advised me to keep my face, but I found this difficult to do.

We did not have a contract, but the government provided us with as much as they could: an office, living space, and sometimes food. We all assumed that it would be easy to engage international businesses in funding this park. In February 1997, a company representative from Exxon invited me to meet with her in Chengdu.

*Flowforms: Water always moves in a vortex motion.
These flowforms encourage this movement.*

Children playing in flowforms

I was dumbfounded when the conversation abruptly ended after a month. Later we learned that around March of that same year, ExxonMobil had decided to no longer fund environmental projects (they did, however, sponsor race cars). I must have visited over twenty American corporations in Beijing seeking funding, only to be rebuffed by all, sometimes with outrageous letters.

Fortunately, the Dutch offered help for the infrastructure, including donating an expensive pump. Our only success with U.S. companies was with American Standard, who agreed to fund the bathrooms for the park. American Standard insisted on installing their seated flush toilets, while the Chinese only wanted squat toilets. The squat toilet is easier to clean and has no risk of a dirty seat. The bathroom would contain two of each. However, within a year, the seated toilets were clogged and filthy; the squat toilets are still fully functioning after twenty-five years.

On a cold, damp day in November 1997, we were all huddled in the concrete room of the offices above the park. Zhang Jihai was pleading with the leaders of the construction teams to get the park done. He had put his career on the line to build the Living Water Garden. It was a difficult time, and fortunately Jon and I had chosen to stay. There were many last-minute details and decisions to attend to. Most of the people involved had never done such a complex construction project, so few understood the importance of details.

On a gorgeous spring day in April 1998, three of us were biking to the park. We expressed our collective amazement that the park had been built. An old woman sat at the entrance to the park, selling jasmine. With a great smile, she gave us a big thumbs up. We were there to witness the testing of the water systems. Everyone held their breath, some with fingers crossed or whispering a silent prayer. The water was turned on. It flowed into the settling pond, then into the first flowforms and down into the cleaning pond. Soon water filled the entire system, all the way down into the fish pond. Grins larger than life appeared on everyone's faces and we began to cheer. In true Chinese style, we went to eat a good meal in celebration. Few moments are so deeply etched in my mind.

Mr. Sun, the senior engineer and coordinator between the different engineering companies, was responsible for the construction. He said to me after the park was finished, "The Living Water Garden was one of the most difficult projects I've worked on. But Betsy never missed any details." He learned to think about water.

The park was visited by governors and mayors from every province in China. In the long review process, Zhang Jihai was praised as an independent thinker who did something very good for the people and was rewarded with a high governing position in the city. Although Zhu Rong Ji, the Premier of China, had opposed the park two years earlier, after visiting it, he declared it the best thing to happen in China.

In July, we all celebrated with an evening of food, drinks, and laughter. We exchanged honest stories that we could not tell during the building process. We learned that Huang Shida had written thirty-four letters to the government insisting that the park be a real bioengineered cleaning system, not just a superficially ecological project.

The Living Water Garden is still functioning twenty-five years later, and is studied in design schools to this day. It demonstrated how powerful nature is when we work according to the interdependence of all systems. Three months after the opening of the park, as we stood watching the waters flow, the plants already flourishing and the wildlife returning, we were stunned to see a kingfisher diving into the wetlands in search of food. Frogs croaked, and many species of birds found homes. The plants in the garden reflected local biodiversity. The project had evolved so quickly that no one had time to digest what we were really doing. Above all, it inspired many people to think about ecosystems, and to consider their waters and make efforts to restore them—not just in China, but around the world.

The Living Water Garden is about to be renovated and is now home to Jane Goodall's Roots and Shoots project.

The biggest innovation in the Living Water Garden is its connectivity. How do you measure the value of connectivity? Bio-dynamism. Designing a large park with many water features is not the same as designing a system of different water features that are all connected: fountains to streams to lakes, all in one system. Disconnecting the parts prevents them from working together for a living environment. This model of connectivity was not immediately adopted by design and planning teams who were trained in single-purpose design.

Shortly after that, I was invited to accompany Tian Jun, assistant to Zhang Jihai, to Beijing to meet with an unnamed person. I asked Zhang Xuehua, my translator, "Who are we going to visit?" She said that he was, as she could describe him best, the Alan Greenspan of China. His name was Yu Guang Yuan. Among his many roles, he was Deng Xiaoping's right-hand advisor in opening up China economically to the world. He started the first environmental group in China at a time when the public stance was to "develop first, clean up later," using the U.S. as a model. When he heard about the Living Water Garden, he flew to Chengdu to see it, and was carried around, as he could no longer walk. It was a tremendous privilege to be able to meet him. Little did I know that my encounter with him would deeply influence my next step in China.

Arriving on a narrow street in an old section of Beijing, we walked through a large old wooden gate into an ancient courtyard full of potted plants. There, we entered a spacious room where Yu Guang Yuan sat behind a large wooden desk. The walls were covered with handwritten scrolls, and his many honors. First he told jokes, and showed me three bundles of one-inch-long pencil stubs wrapped in rubber bands—all the pencils he had used to write his books. Each stub was a trophy of his work. He asked me if I knew what I had done. I started to explain the park, but

Living Water Garden, aerial view

Constructed wetlands

Stepping down to the river

he firmly interrupted me and said, "I will tell you what you have done. Most people come to China to make money and steal our culture. You came and gave us a future. Now you must come to Beijing, because all good ideas spread from here." Tears were streaming down my face.

After the completion of the Living Water Garden, I discovered its impact. I was invited to university campuses and city planning bureaus around China where students and faculty showed me wetlands that were used for tertiary treatment or stormwater collection. After I visited for three days with the planning bureau of Nanning City, Guangxi Province, they decided to keep their rivers intact and not develop right up to the edge of their beautiful and productive lake. Years later, the ideas behind the Living Water Garden were showing up in other parts of China.

Living Water Garden

Back in the United States, I was invited to speak at universities and organizations. When I spoke at MIT or Carnegie Mellon, I was surprised to find out that the engineers rarely bothered to learn about the ecology of the places in which they might design. Hopefully this has changed, though the current impulse is still to engineer single solutions when more integrated, sustainable solutions would not only be more effective but usually cheaper in the long run. Haung Shi Da began doing many projects, primarily creating biological systems for wastewater from schools and villages. Tian Jun founded the Chengdu Urban Rivers Association to clean the upstream waters. In the years that followed, it was not unusual for me to be invited to a university or middle school that would show me their water capture and cleaning system.

The Impossible is Possible

In this chapter, I have detailed one extended creative experience, stepping into the unknown and listening. It was my good fortune that I could follow the possibilities presented and the connections that showed up. However, without the first step, nothing would have happened. The world is full of such openings, especially when  you do not have an exact plan, only hunches and a vision.

Artists can think outside boxes, unconstrained by regulations. We can imagine, envision, be flexible, and follow those paths that are not yet clear. You do not need to know the engineering to imagine, or to experiment. You do not need to know what you might do if you head in a certain direction, or even prove it can work before you try. The direction I headed in was to be an artist acting for ecosystems and taught by water.

Take a minute to think for yourself. Notice what popped into your mind! An idea. Whatever idea you have, whether you know how to write it or draw it—share it. Ask the question, *can we..? How can we do this? What would happen if...? Can we get our community to agree/honor...? How can we make our available waters visible? Can we return them to living systems? What is a living system?* Caring for our earth could become the biggest art project we do; our biggest collaboration. Although the projects will take place in separate locations, all waters are connected and there will be a tipping point when those waters begin to work together.

ART is the Change AGenT of the WoRLD

Working in Community

Every community needs to empower itself to work with its waters to ensure sustainability. This important job cannot be left in the hands of a few "experts." Everyone needs to know what is in their water, where their water comes from, and how much water is available. Every water system, from entire watersheds to backyards, can utilize the principles of collaboration and complexity. There are many obstacles to face: who receives good water and who does not; the incredible drive to materialize everything, regardless of the impact on people and ecosystems; and cycles of colonialism and dominance. Right now, we have to face the magnitude of a superstructure controlled by corporations that function to maximize profit.

So many of the people I've spoken with after lectures could not imagine beginning. They'd say, "I'd like to do something, *but*..."—then excuses and more excuses. "How will I survive?" seems to come before "How will *we* survive?" Covid-19 is a symptom of too much loss of biodynamic systems. Stronger viruses are predicted in the future. To become resilient in the face of challenges like these, we must change how we live, care for each other, and restore our ecosystems.

It's not easy to do, but not impossible. It *is* difficult to change the habits we have developed and to learn different habits. All the rules and regulations were made by us human beings. We can change the rules, adapt them to what is needed, and make them work toward a biodynamic earth. It was illegal to recycle gray water in California until 1992. Why? Did people believe that water that had been in a shower was bad for plants? For twenty-five years, a group taught people how to reuse their gray water and clean it a bit through a natural system. That was illegal until a large drought prompted the government to change the regulations. It makes sense to recycle our gray water, especially to be used in gardens. Plants love the extra nutrients.

WETLAND GARDENS
for GRAY WATER MANAGEMENT

START TALKING ABOUT
WATER

YOU DON'T THINK
ABOUT WATER UNTIL
YOU DON'T HAVE IT.

Empowering people to take charge of their waters was at the front of my mind. Lecturing and visiting universities was one form of action. Over and over, I discovered how resistant structures are to change. Some professors tried hard but had little effect and were understandably discouraged. Students were eager to pick up a shovel and start planting. But school administrators and boards of directors held students back. Administrators prevented meaningful projects like changing lawns into productive landscapes, or parking lots into swales that could capture and clean rainwater. They also opposed essential measures like going energy-neutral and adding recycling to dining halls. Art departments could see the infinite creative possibilities of marrying art and science, but few could go there.

In my experience, people are eager to talk about water. "Let's talk about water" usually gathers a crowd. Depending on the neighborhood, it invites a diversity of people, class backgrounds, cultures, professions, and skill sets. This invitation to notice water is the beginning of building a group that can create a groundswell of activism. Getting to know people, sharing ideas, and brainstorming together can take you further than you would go on your own. Depending on your group, you will choose what to do and where to begin.

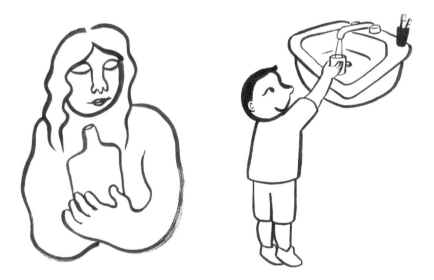

Great questions to start with: *Where does your water come from? Where does your water go? What filters water? What is rainwater collection?* Municipal water treatment systems are also a great topic to start with. If your community is facing a specific issue, that can be a great way to launch into broader topics. Begin with a visit to a nearby body of water—a wetland, river, or wastewater treatment plant. You can also do projects yourself, like installing rain barrels, planting rain gardens, or changing your driveway and walkways to permeable surfaces that allow the water to return to the ground. By doing these things yourself, you can demonstrate to others what is possible.

Each neighborhood can learn about their waters first, because

factors like where you live, how much rain falls, or what's harming rivers will determine what you do. Each home and its surroundings are part of a larger system, called a watershed. Understanding the larger picture makes it clear what needs to happen. Start with your watershed—your greater situation. Mapping helps you see which problems in your watershed are the most important, and what kind of solutions your big picture requires. For example, maybe too much water is running off the uplands, because they have lots of hardscape (concrete, asphalt, roads, and driveways), causing pipes to overflow and creating flooding downstream. Those pipes deliver the water into streams, rather than letting the water be absorbed into the land.

Regardless of how you start, every beginning will lead you and your group to look at your watershed. Ask questions about where your water comes from and where it goes. No matter where you live, you are in a watershed together with a community of people and other living beings who share the waters.

There are many ways to structure a meeting. The following is my approach. I change things depending on the size and composition of the group. Start with a vision that places water as the foundation of the future of the community. These are suggestions, not rules. My intention is to discover who is in the room, and what skills they bring. The  amount of time per introduction may depend on how large the group is or how informal you like to be. If your group is large, keep it short:

- Name
- Why they came to the meeting
- Something about themselves
- Something they would like to see happen in their community

If your group is large, with no central focus, you can gather everyone together to discover their interests then divide them into small groups by topic. You can also create a list of the most common topics of interest and allow people to join whichever group they choose.

Small Group Discussion Ideas:

- Planning a cleanup project
- Creating an art event
- Discovering our stormwater system
- Mapping our waters
- Discovering our watershed

When each group reports, you will have a picture of people's concerns and ideas. These can be written on a large piece of paper. Hold a discussion about where to begin. See where you have consensus to start. If the group is large enough, there might be more than one idea that gets started and this is good. Generate a list of those participants who are interested in certain ideas. I have found it best if each group has a leader who ensures that you meet, and that people share the initiative.

Take a walk in the rain and follow the storm flow.

How do we know if there's lead in our pipes?

Join active groups or raise water issues in other groups:

- Farmers' market groups and consumers
- Audubon Society and other environmental groups
- Sierra Club
- Garden groups
- Community activists
- University students studying ecology and biology
- School educational programs
- Research labs
- Arts organizations
- Religious community groups including churches, synagogues, and mosques
- Community board groups
- Landscape architecture companies
- Solar and other green energy companies
- Recycling groups and centers
- Museums and botanical gardens
- Urban farmers
- Neighborhood organizations
- People operating water infrastructure

An Example of a Water Workshop

While searching for clues as to how to structure community water workshops, I turned to water as the collaborative element between all living forms. How could water's equitable nature be taken as a model for community projects?

Everyone interested in water is invited to the workshop. Scientists, artists, citizens, activists, government officials, and planners need to come together.

1. Workshops are planned with the community. People in the community who have specific knowledge about your water could be asked to give the presentations. For example, if pollution is a problem, invite a scientist, perhaps a biologist, who has been studying the situation.
2. In the workshop, a collective community process is used to decide which projects to initiate and how to use available resources.
3. The workshop is concluded by deciding where and how to start.
4. I do not select the projects to be done. The community or the artists who have projects decide how to spend the money.

Water quality workshop in Chengdu

Recently, I've started asking workshop participants about their ethnic and cultural identities. Without exception, the more people are invited to share who they are and take pride in their heritage, the more ideas come forward, and the more relationships across cultures are formed. People feel as though they have the space to show and share their thinking. I have been pleased with the results.

I have invited people to speak in an order like this:

- People who do not identify as white go first. It might surprise you who raises their hand because it is not always obvious who comes from what heritage. Recent immigrants—third generation or sooner—speak next.  This is often a large group that can be subdivided further into the countries of origin.
- Everyone else follows, also identifying their backgrounds.

Sometimes I invite the quietest person or the youngest to speak first. Everyone answers the following questions:

- What is your name?
- Identity or country your people came from?
- What is something you like about your culture?

Next, I have everyone divide into small groups of about four people each, with those of similar backgrounds in the same group.

Each person in the group has five minutes, more or less, without interruption, to talk about themselves: who they are and what they would like for themselves in the next two hours.

Everyone returns to the larger group. I give a short talk on the topic for the workshop—our waters, your waters, etc.— and what might be possible.

Again groups are formed, this time around issues and concerns that are proposed. All ideas are written on a paper, and then people select a group of interest. If eight people want the same group, then there can be two groups for that interest. They listen to each other talk about what they would like to do. At this stage, all ideas are good ideas.

Put a piece of paper on the wall and ask people to write, to draw, to imagine. Gather many together to create a vision that might not exist without your group.

If you start at the grassroots level, you will eventually need engineers. If you start at the engineering level, you will eventually need the grassroots.

Starting with the grassroots ensures that inclusion is built into the process. People come into the project with an understanding of their own situation and desire to do things for their situation. Many decisions about your water are made at the level of engineering or profiteering. Citizens are rarely included in or informed about these processes until after decisions have been made.

However, there are usually people within your local government structures who want to hear from and work with community groups and grassroots activities. You can also find allies among people who work with relevant companies or nonprofit organizations.

Each community lives in a unique setting with its own weather patterns, geological setting, and developmental situation. When you're ready, contact people who understand your situation on a complex level. For example, if you are in a desert area, you will need to find someone who understands the desert, where the water goes, what plants hold the water in the ground or in themselves. Where is the flow? How can farmers water their crops correctly? I try to invite scientists familiar with the local situation, as well as people who have found ways to live in—and with—the desert.

I developed many skills in response to a situation, to a vision, to an urge to work with a particular river or place, or to collaborate with a community. I asked myself: *What is the culture here? What are the values of this group?* I try to avoid thinking that my culture is better or that I know best. It has been important to my work that I learn about the culture and the science of a particular place, and find the people who have studied the plants, species, and exact geographic facts of that place, and the waters.

Case Study: An Artist Acts
Lake Clean-up Project in Maravatío, Michoacán, Mexico

In three short weeks, Beth Grossman created a cleanup of a lake that supplied water to a farming community.

In the spring of 2017, Beth was given the opportunity to spend three weeks at the Guapamacátaro Center for Art and Ecology near Maravatío, Michoacán, Mexico. The director, Alicia Marván, invited each artist to create a participatory project with the local community, with which she'd had a long relationship.

Beth walked around Laguna del Fresno, meeting locals and talking to the farmers, young people, and their mothers. Together they admired how beautiful the lake was and lamented that it was filled with plastic garbage that was poisoning the fish. Litter was degrading on the floodplain that horses and cattle used for grazing. Most agreed that it was a serious problem.

She then invited students to paint what they loved about their lake and talked to citizens in front of the school and church. A date was set, Saturday morning, June 10, 2017, to hold the cleanup "party." Through word of mouth, flyers, and announcements, the farmers were asked to bring their large empty feed bags. The mayor was happy to assist, and helped by making announcements on the town loudspeaker and organizing the pick-up of the garbage bags after the event.

Cleanup and making art

On the morning of the cleanup party, thirty participants gathered with excitement, and joined in teams to compete for the most garbage gathered. In just ninety minutes, a large swath of the floodplain was cleaned up and about forty huge sacks were filled with muddy garbage. Cleaning up the land proved to be instantly gratifying, and many remarked that they could feel the lake sparkling back with appreciation.

Fruit trees were awarded as prizes to each team to plant in their gardens. The elementary students' team decided to plant their tree in the schoolyard.

After cleaning up the lake, we discussed some possible next steps to care for Laguna del Fresno:

1. Work with the mayor to host this lake cleanup party after each rainy season.
2. Design a campaign to create awareness about the impact of litter on the lake and wildlife, which are precious resources for the entire community.
3. Study where the dumping is coming from.
4. Strategize projects that could help put a stop to dumping and littering in the first place.
5. Install public garbage cans around the lake with regular transfer of trash to the dump.
6. Lobby the local government to provide funds for the Public Works Department to safely remove the existing litter from the waters.
7. Monitor the effects of the ongoing cleanup on the lake, wildlife, and the land.
8. Share this information with other communities.

If we reduce what living with, and for, the life on this planet means, these would be our big guideposts:

- **col·lab·o·ra·tion**—the action of working with someone to produce or create something.
- **co·op·er·a·tion**—the process of working together to the same end.
- **com·mu·ni·ty**—a group of people living in the same place or having a characteristic in common.
- **com·plex·i·ty**—the state or quality of being intricate or complicated; order on the edge of chaos.

Case Study: Sounds of Water

From 2001 to 2006, I traveled between Beijing and San Francisco, with San Francisco as my base. Early in 2002, Jan Peterson invited me to create a water feature in Redding, California's Turtle Bay Exploration Park. I asked her if they had sufficient water, and she told me that they would have water forever. Nevertheless, I made a low water use installation that recycles the waters through a natural filtering system. In *Sounds of Water*, water pours out from a high point on one of the standing stones, symbolizing waters descending from the mountains. This water meets the waters bubbling out of a living water sculpture, a spring. These waters are distributed in three directions representing local statistics on water usage. One direction represents domestic use, totaling 8% of total flow; another represents industrial use at 21%; and the third agricultural use at 71%. Carved into the granite slabs and concrete is information about water usage in Redding. Carved into the industrial section is information about how much water it takes to make steel, and in the agricultural section about how much is required to make a loaf of bread. In the central section, where the water flows, international statistics are carved in the stones. Classes still visit *Sounds of Water*, staying to learn for a couple of hours. In 2016, there was a big drought, and all water features at the arboretum except *Sounds of Water* had to be shut down.

Water talks to us every day. Often it speaks silently through our bodies: thirst, sweat, heartbeat, and breath. Water gurgles, drips, sloshes, and murmurs. It splashes and splatters in kitchens, bathrooms, laundries, and gardens. Water descends from the sky, drumming on surfaces, washing everything gently or with a determined force.

*Sounds of Water at
Turtle Bay Arboretum*

Persisting in the U.S.

As a visiting artist at a number of universities and colleges, I've found that universities and colleges sometimes have a token energy-efficient building, a student-initiated garden, and a few examples of low-energy use and recycling. However, during my travels at this time, I did not find an educational institution that had implemented sufficient changes for sustainability. One school had lawns so big that a tractor had to run every day of the week to cut the grass. Dow Chemical funds this college. Chemicals used to maintain the lawns killed all insects, so few birds could be seen. Lawns that do little except require chemicals (and vast amounts of precious water) serve no purpose.

There were teachers and students dedicated to preserving and restoring their local natural world and who were understandably often very discouraged.

Small-group projects informed and taught many who might go on to learn more. Small vegetable gardens were for introducing students who came from urban environments. At one college, we started a rainwater collection project. These projects need to be connected to broader, more comprehensive efforts. The time has come to act on a large scale. We must restore the complexity in our lands, reconnecting creeks to rivers, rivers to wetlands, and wetlands to oceans. Hand in hand with water, we must restore the forests by planting billions of trees.

Over the years, teaching and doing projects, I noticed that engineering was getting more and more aggressive. Water bottling was increasing rapidly and consciousness of water was disappearing. I noticed how difficult it was for people to think about water.

On the upside, the earth rights movement—which is promoting the personhood of rivers—is gaining steam. In recent years, many people are fighting to protect their water. Around the world this struggle is constant. The Maori of New Zealand and Standing Rock Sioux in the Dakotas are just two examples of people protecting

their land and waters from a polluting pipeline, mining, or appro-
priation of waters for large cities.

A Trustworthy Public Water Supply

Public water supplies in the U.S.
are regulated under the Safe Drinking Water Act (SDWA), which requires
publicizing annual reports on the treatment and quality of municipal drinking
water. Bottled water is a product, not
a publicly serviced utility, so it is not
regulated by the SDWA but rather by
the regulations of the FDA. The FDA
regulates bottled water as a food, and
doesn't require water bottling companies to disclose the source of their
water, their treatment methods, or any
potential contaminants. While the FDA

checks bottling companies' water, the companies do not have to
report quality violations themselves.[11] In fact, about 25% or more
of bottled water is tap water.[12]

The public's fear of health issues is real and has also created mis-
conceptions about water. This fear has been exploited at times, and
at other times under-acknowledged—and has torpedoed the idea
of the water fountain,[13] and created doubts about the benefits of a
public water supply. Cities removed their drinking water fountains
after water-bottling companies financed campaigns, falsely claiming
that their water was cleaner. Water-bottling companies profit from
failures in municipal water supplies. The cleanliness of fountains
was challenged, but now new drinking fountain designs prevent the
transmission of disease. Maintaining a clean public water supply is
imperative for social equity. Paris has installed drinking water fountains throughout the city.

"The biosphere is a biosphere because it is a hydrosphere.
The planet's hydrologic cycle is a water democracy—
a system of distributing water for all species…"
—VANDANA SHIVA

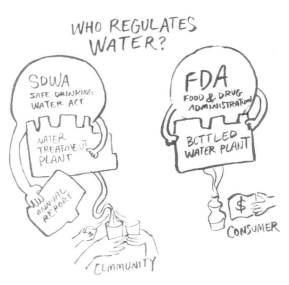

To answer the question of what water I drink: I drink the tap water in New York. I use a water filter in my home as a precaution, because I know that the water supply varies in what it contains. I try to carry my own water bottle, and I challenge myself to travel without buying a bottle of water. Water bottling is creating a gigantic chain of problems, from the destruction of the environment where the water is bottled, to the transportation of the water to sell, to the enormous mess of those plastic bottles, which most likely will not be recycled.

We cannot talk about the bottling industry without talking about racism and classism. Bottling companies present a high health risk to America's disenfranchised. This is largely a result of the soft drink industry's practice of bombarding poor communities with advertising. A study conducted by the *American Journal of Preventive Medicine* finds that soda companies go as far as timing advertisements for sugary drinks to coincide with the days leading up to the monthly distribution of food stamp benefits.[14] Coca-Cola has reached a net worth of 232 billion dollars by profiting off of people living pay-check-to-paycheck. Nestlé strategically creates bottling facilities where they know the water supply is very limited, then sells the bottles to the population which has lost its meager supply. In these situations, not only must the bottling factory close but all the inhab-itants need to adopt measures like low water loss, rainwater collec-tion, and gray water recycling.

The bottling industry's racism and classism extend far beyond the local corner store. The pollution caused by plastic bottle manu-facturing disproportionately affects poorer communities, whose concerns are dismissed when factories are built.[15] And the bottling industry's deliberate misinformation campaign, which has sought to portray public water supplies as "dirty," has discouraged investment in our water supplies. This has contributed to public health crises such as the water problems in Flint, Michigan.

As America grapples with the racism at its very core, companies like Coca-Cola are putting out statements that "Black Lives Matter." Meanwhile, Coca-Cola continues to commit human rights abuses around the world, mostly against people of color.[16] The current moment should be more than just a branding opportunity.

When we say racism is "systemic," we mean that racism is inher-ent to the entire system. We must remain distrustful of Fortune 500 companies' focus-grouped public statements on racism. What does it mean for Coca-Cola to tweet that Black Lives Matter when Coca-Cola continues to be the worst plastics polluter in the his-tory of the planet?[17] Plastic pollu-tion inherently targets communi-ties of color around the globe. What does it mean for Nestlé to criticize "the senseless racism that tears into the fabric of our com-munities" when Nestlé continues

to steal water from Indigenous people?[18] "Systemic racism" can only be fought with systemic change; anything less is hypocrisy.

Right now, water bottling companies are searching for pristine groundwater, buying up rights to that water, pumping it out into a truck and sending it to a new bottling factory. Nestlé states clearly their strategy to survive for 150 years; we will buy up all the water we can, and bottle it—after all, people will always need water.

Many communities, including some in Maine and California, are fighting back against these companies. Michigan's Osceola Township, for example, has been fighting a drawn-out battle with Nestlé over the company's proposed pumping station. In the fall of 2019, Osceola Township won a huge victory when a Michigan court ruled that Nestlé's bottling operations do not constitute a public service.

All communities need to consider putting into law their right to their own waters. Ideally, each community needs to own its water. Such revolutionary legislation would need to be a public process. We need to debate foundational questions: How do we price water? Do we have a graduated water tax? Do those with less receive a part of water for free? All the communities who have fought off the takeover of their waters need to form a network of shared experiences. If we think logically about the extraction of water from a place, and the conse-  quences for the life in that place, and for the people who need the waters, taking it is equivalent to genocide.

The dominant conversation around water is summed up by these two words: "clean" or "unclean." But these terms are misleading. "Clean" is more about human safety than it is about quality. Plenty of species cannot live in what we call clean water. Instead, they need living water. Salamanders, frogs, and small water invertebrates are like the wetlands' canary in the coal mine. Trump's 2018 decision to roll back the Clean Water Act[19] has impacted species that depend upon good water quality to thrive.

What is "alive" water? Alive water contains minerals and good microbes. It is also oxygenated by movement. Eagles, whales, fish, and humans all need living water. Purified water or water that is treated with chlorines, dioxide, ozone, and fluoride to keep it clean is not alive, and it is not good for humans to drink regularly. Purified water removes much-needed minerals from the human body. People can filter their water instead. Finally, plastic bottles discharge plastic into the water, and bits of plastic can be found suspended in the bottle.[20]

Waterborne diseases have been with humans since the beginning of history (e.g. cholera and diphtheria). We have extended our fear of water-borne disease to all water-borne microbes, even those that can keep us healthy.

Now we think of clean or "pure" water as water without the life it should contain; this ideal is reflected in treatment systems' efforts to sterilize water, which is a single-purpose design for wiping out bacteria. America's water problems are worse than many people assume. Mil-lions of Americans are facing higher and higher water bills, all while water quality is falling.[21] A survey of 12 cities found an average increase of 80% in water bill costs over the past 8 years. "More people are in trouble, and the poorest of the poor are in big trouble," says Roger Colton, a leading utilities analyst. "The data shows that

PUBLIC
WATER

we've got an affordability problem in an overwhelming number of cities nation-wide that didn't exist a decade ago."[22] Meanwhile, federal water bill aid has plummeted, and the consequences of cli-mate chaos—specifically, droughts—are bringing massive disruptions to water sources.

In America—the richest country on earth—1.7 million people lack access to basic plumbing like toilets, showers, or running water.[23] The Covid-19 pandemic threatens to raise that number, since high unemployment means more and more people won't be able to pay the bills to keep their water on. "At this rate," write Senator Bernie Sanders and Congresswoman Brenda Lawrence, "more than a third of American households may not be able to afford their water bills five years from now."[24]

America's water crisis is yet another example of society's most vul-nerable paying the price for the climate destruction caused by the most powerful. Water must become a human right for real change to happen.

Wastewater

We need to honor wastewater treatment; it's the heart of every community. Wastewater treatment eliminates diseases—it lets us live together in cities. A wastewater treatment plant is as important as the hospital, school, or library to a community, and yet it is treated as an eyesore, something to be hidden from view. Wastewater treat-ment is an ever-evolving technology—pushing to increase efficiency and repurpose its byproducts. Generally wastewater treatment is still handled with old technologies on the edge of a river and pro-duces a low-quality final product.

*Monk collecting water; this water will not be clean if
pesticides or fertilizers are used in the surrounding landscape.*

If wastewater systems were built in all communities, and if there
were small inexpensive ones, then those communities would control their waste and waters. They would have a reusable byproduct
that nurtures the living system. There are many technologies from
"natural" processes to high-tech engineered ones. A combination of
these two is now most common. Everything from digging a hole and
leaving your waste in the ground to fertilize a tree, to large industrial
bio-digesting units in a crowded city, are forms of treatment.

It's important to know that solid waste—poop, from people and
animals—does not dissolve in water; it dissolves in dirt and can be
 converted into a useful product.
Human urine is a very good
nutrient; when diluted properly,
it is the best fertilizer you can
have. Ideally, most of the products from wastewater treatment
can be reused. Yet there are now

some things entering the system which are hard to remove, such as estrogens, antibiotics, hospital wastes, nanoparticles, and, in some places, numerous poisons.

Learn about your wastewater treatment plant and what the right technology is for your situation. Old plants were placed near rivers and streams that carry away the treated sewage. This is no longer a viable solution. The U.S. requires a dilution of 1:5, which is not sufficient to keep bodies of water clean. Canada requires 1:10, which is much better.

Some processes use plants, oxygen, and microbes to effectively

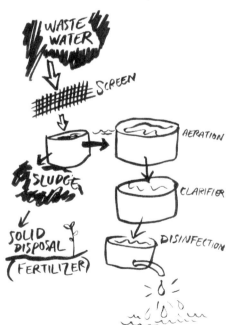

treat human waste—these are called "living systems." These processes draw inspiration from the structures of streams and wetlands—natural models of wastewater treatment. Most inspiring are the companies that are recycling nearly everything to be reused.

We learn about the costs of our lifestyle by learning about our wastewater. Given the state of our waters right now, we need to have a near-zero pollution policy. Let's stop negotiating with the health of the planet. Let's live with our mosquitos, bees, and all the things that bite, and that the birds eat.

Rather than single large facilities, resilience and quality are enhanced when wastewater treatment plants are small and local. There are now excellent underground systems that could be in parks, golf courses, and large gardens, where the cleaned waters could be used for watering. Integrating wastewater into our lives and the environment is basic, and will become a necessary part of designing for resilience.

A visit to the wastewater treatment plant is great for most classes or groups of citizens. Ask yourself: how can you make these essential treatment plants a place of celebration and education, honored in your community? Start a discussion with them, and think together about what can be done to create community awareness. Wastewater treatment facilities have great potential for art and science projects.

Let's consider chemicals. Over 84,000 chemicals have been invented in recent times, and we have tested the environmental safety of only 1%. These chemicals are everywhere—water is used to create them, and contaminated water is discharged after they are made. Chemicals leach into our waters all the time from thousands of products, extractions, fertilizers, and repellants, to name a few.

If you live in a remote place, don't assume that your water is safe. Your well can become polluted by many sources: from factories or various businesses, to what farmers use on their crops, to apparently benign products you use in your everyday life.

There is no way to absolutely isolate a polluted body of water. Waters left over from a frack two miles deep eventually find their

The wastewater treatment process

draws its inspiration from the structures of streams & wetlands.

way into other water bodies. There is no such thing as isolating polluted water. Water will find its way eventually through solid rock. Nuclear power may be a way to reduce carbon emissions by replacing oil and coal, but it is incredibly dangerous. In the hundreds of thousands of years that it takes for nuclear waste to become safe, water will constantly be boring through the walls we put around it. This reality makes it abundantly clear that clean energy is our only option. We need to consider long-term solutions: solar, wind, and tidal energy; wave hydropower, micro hydropower, geothermal energy. Clean energy is not just about energy; it's also about water.

Each community needs to be able to take charge of its waters. It is imperative to evolve a collective consciousness that water cannot be controlled for the sake of short-term profit or the salvation of a few. We need policies and regulations on an international level that eliminate the hoarding of water supplies.

Mapping

A map is knowledge of the past, the present, and the possible future. Mapping provides information about your waters: where they are, how large they are, their flows, and the changes over time caused by development or natural disasters. Most importantly, you can see where and how you might start a project for your waters.

Types of Maps

Most people can read and understand street maps, but many cannot read other types of maps and wouldn't even consider looking at a topographic, surface water, or water infrastructure map.

Street maps: A street map is the most recognizable map, mostly used for navigation. You will use street maps in your mapping sessions to guide you and your fellow community members by pointing out familiar places and locating features from other maps around the streets you recognize.

Topographic maps: Like a street map, topographic maps show major roads, populated areas, and areas of development. They show forest cover in green, along with waterways and borders. But most important, topographic maps use concentric contours to illustrate elevation. Contour lines illustrate slope—and therefore indicate the natural movement of water runoff through the landscape, down hills, through valleys, around cliffs, and in rivers and streams.

Water infrastructure maps: These maps reveal the potable water supply systems and storm-sewer pipes that underlie our streets and buildings, as well as the ditches and other water conveyance structures designed to remove runoff. Discovering where pipes, sewer lines, flood controls, and engineered systems are located helps us understand how our natural waters have been drastically redirected and modified—and allows us to imagine how to reconnect and restore our water systems.

GIS (Geographic Information Systems) is computer software for presenting information about a geographic area. It is used to create many types of maps. It enables us to determine where pipe systems leak or spill over, and where interventions should be placed. GIS technology is a powerful tool that anyone can learn to use.

Other types of maps include geological maps (to explain the path of water through soil and bedrock), economic maps for area income (because too often access to good water is divided economically) and zoning maps (which explain permitted land uses).

It is always good to ask what a map might *not* be showing you.

Historical Maps

Historical maps reveal how our relationships with our geography and ecosystems have changed over time. Many cities have archives of maps, some hundreds of years old. Showing historic maps to present-day communities can lead to changes in how we think about our water systems, along with new conversations.

When considering a design, it's useful to compare pre-development versus post-development circumstances. Old maps can reveal the surrounding environment as it once existed, and this can inform what you decide to do now. You may discover that your town's shopping complex was built over a wetland.

As our cities expanded, brooks and streams were covered and diverted through pipes; the names given to the sewers often reveal the original water source (for example, "Freshwater Brook Sewer"). Old landfills, early industrial areas, railway yards, and other land uses that required large areas of flat land were frequently placed on infilled wetlands. One use of this information could be to locate a stream that has been buried and daylight it—that is, restore it.

Each location presents different challenges and solutions based on its unique ecological and human history. When I began working in Pittsburgh, one of my first destinations was the Heinz Historical Library. There I found maps dating back hundreds of years, including Indigenous maps. These older maps show a landscape full of small streams and springs. Now, none of these smaller

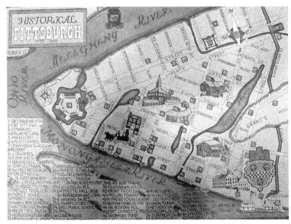

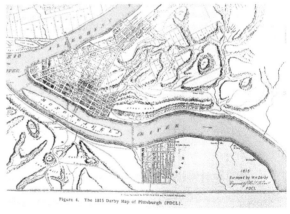

Figure 4. The 1815 Darby Map of Pittsburgh (PDCL).

waterways can be found. At least fifty-six streams have been buried or put into pipes, and one no longer hears the sound of water running in the city. The consequences of this include small streams that can no longer service their local ecosystems—they are jettisoned into large bodies of water, at times creating major flooding events.

Where to Find Maps of Your Region

- Libraries, historical societies, and museums
- City government offices: City Planning, Parks and Recreation, and Transportation and Engineering Offices
- Universities and colleges (libraries and various departments in them: geology, architecture, ecology, history, civil engineering, landscape architecture, geography)
- Municipal water treatment centers
- Not all countries or states have maps readily available; some have restricted access.
- Maps on the Internet; especially Google Maps and (for even more detail) Google Earth

It may be necessary to contact several institutions and companies to find what you're looking for. Unfortunately, sometimes it's simply impossible to find certain maps. Also, few organizations are interested in an overall and complete picture of the water system, so you may need to combine a variety of maps and other sources to delineate the waters in your community.

I've had experiences where relevant maps could not be located. When I was visiting Dillon, Montana in 2016, I had planned to hold two mapping workshops. However, nobody could find maps of the pipes and watersheds of southern Montana. Local historical maps were not readily available, and much information was missing. Dillon is surrounded by copper mines and cattle ranches which contribute to runoff, and Montana's economy is based on mining and extractive industries. Without maps of the infrastructure and a clear view of the watershed, we were unable to trace how these industries might be affecting the city's water and local rivers. As a result, the two workshops became a time when I invited people to meet each other, and brainstorm what they wanted to make happen.

Workshops with Maps

During mapping workshops, people often get excited about locating their homes on a map. Once they've done this, invite community members to talk about the places they see on the map; they might provide a great depth of knowledge from experience, adding layers of information to the maps.

It is useful to have people with different skill sets present. Include a person who knows how to read topographic maps, or someone that can draw and gets excited about design.

Explore local waters with your group. Gathering these observations will help you build your maps further. Go out with members of your group the next time it rains and follow the rainwater, observing where it travels. Or take a walk along the edge of a stream or river. Notice where water moves rapidly. Observe where there are marshy areas or wetlands. This is where water slows

Not everything is online — take a trip to your local library to find out more about your community watershed

Don't be shy — librarians went to school for this and they like helping you research.

I want to know about water

HELP DESK

down and you can see what lives there, and which species like still waters—frogs, bugs, turtles, birds. Your observations will be vital to restoring and designing water systems; you are building your knowledge of what is currently happening, and this is essential to deciding on objectives for your designs.

Below is a series of questions that will help you define your local water system, figure out how it functions, and gauge its health. Some answers will be found in maps, others in the form of local stories, and still others in data collected by conservation organizations or governments.

- Where are the bodies of water in your community: rivers, streams, lakes, ponds, wetlands, reservoirs, springs?
- Who has access to them?
- What kind of life do you find in and around them? Are there sources of pollution near them?
- What did your waters look like in the past? Are they different now?
- How would you describe the topography of your region? Is your land flat, hilly, or mountainous? Do rivers and streams run fast, or slow? In which direction does runoff flow?
- Does stormwater runoff flow into a body of water?
- Are there any businesses or factories that pollute? Where? Does their pollution affect waterways?
- Are there areas where basements flood? Are there areas where people have very little water near their homes?
- Is the water clear? Clarity does not necessarily mean that water is clean. You can find out more about water quality by paying attention to what is growing in the water. Certain plants and insects like clean water—like watercresses and water striders.
- Where does rainwater drain, and where do those drains lead? Watch how rainwater runs off from one property to the next, or down onto the street. Where does water puddle? How quickly do the puddles dry? Where do puddles remain for days, stagnant?

- Where are there permeable surfaces like soil, gravel, and vegetation? Where are there *impermeable* surfaces like pavement, cement, and asphalt? Does rainwater mostly run along paved roads, or over vegetated ground and ditches?
- Where does your wastewater go: to a treatment plant, a river, or a septic system?
- Where is your wastewater treatment plant? How does it work? How often does the system fail or not work? What happens when the treatment plant isn't working or is overloaded?
- Is there a drinking water treatment plant? Where? What chemicals and processes are used to treat drinking water?

When your group works with maps, you will be able to see beyond your own neighborhood to the whole town or city and beyond, to the larger landscape. Just as we can see rainwater flowing from our roof into the gutter, we can now picture where the stormwater flows into a river, where that river flows by another town and eventually into the ocean. It becomes clear that the water that leaves our homes, our community, continues downstream, affecting people and land along the way. Most people I have worked with do not consider where their water goes or where it comes from.

There are larger issues that can be addressed if the public knows their maps. Maybe the impact on Pittsburgh waters from fracking might have been avoided if the public were engaged in where or whether to frack. But there has been little public outcry to fracking. The claims that there is a "safe" way to frack are false. Water will always seep into the cracks created by fracking, then find their way to other water sources. Public consciousness on hydraulic fracking is changing, though, with Ireland recently becoming the fourth country—after France, Germany, and Bulgaria—to ban the practice outright.

In Logan, Utah, during a couple of two-hour workshops with students and faculty, the participants were shocked by what they learned. In this water-challenged state, the campus used water as though it were an endless supply. After studying the maps of the city sewers and surrounding waters, we focused on the campus water systems. To our shock, there was a vast network of pipes that delivered water for lawns, rain or shine. The groups came up with many possible interventions on the campus. Ideas flowed about how to capture rainwater and bring attention to local issues concerning water. The same week we learned that Salt Lake City is proposing taking the waters from Logan for the city. That would be a large transfer of water.

Living Waters of Larimer

> *"If I had an hour to solve a problem and my life depended on the solution, I would spend the first fifty-five minutes determining the proper question to ask, for once I know the proper question, I could solve the problem in less than five minutes."*
> —ALBERT EINSTEIN

Living Waters of Larimer began with an installation at a well-known alternative arts space, the Mattress Factory, in Pittsburgh. I agreed to participate, on the condition that I could initiate a community-based project. In my search, I did not find a community that was interested in addressing water. However, I discovered that almost all of Pittsburgh's streams were in pipes. Its wetlands and lakes had been drained and no one in the community was addressing their water issues. Flooding was constant, and water infrastructure problems were growing.

Finally, I met a woman from Pittsburgh at a workshop in Brooklyn who told me about a Pittsburgh neighborhood called Larimer. She directed me to Fred Brown, a leader with the Dynamic Transition Movement. Thanks to Fred's leadership, the community had created a vision for the neighborhood to become sustainable in its food, energy, and water. The neighborhood's food and energy situations were understood although not implemented—but water? I began by meeting with Carolyn Peeks, leader of the Green Team, and a couple of other people. At a meeting, Carolyn quickly proposed a name: Living Waters of Larimer. In our initial discussions, we focused on several questions: Where does water go? What can be done with it? How do we currently use it? Where, and how, can we capture this water?

Larimer was built on a flat, unique plateau and was beloved for its large churches and historic houses. Once a thriving and diverse community, it was now a struggling, predominantly Black district. The community was made up of people passionate about its history, people who were fighting hard for their vision of revitalization. A large part of that vision was to transition to renewable energy, and sustainable food and water. Contrary to all-too-common classist beliefs, values like these do not need to be externally imposed by the privileged and powerful. In fact, most of them have originated among the disenfranchised, who know all too well how exploited they are and what they need: good food, and clean water.

The Larimer community was full of savvy, energetic survivors with their own ideas on how to fight gentrification and implement the fair allocation of resources within the community. Larimer was filled with vacant lots and crumbling buildings. The community was fighting an uphill battle against prevailing top-down, own-it-or-lose-it power structures. It is not an exaggeration to say that classism and racism dominated the landscape.

Community garden in Larimer

A new community center, complete with a gym and a large swimming pool, became a focal point for programs to revitalize the neighborhood. Fred Brown insisted on a swimming pool, so that young Black children, who in some cases were taught to fear water, could learn to swim. Fear of water, rivers, and oceans was great, as those bodies of water were the arteries of the slave trade.

There I was, an older white woman, talking to people about water in a community where basements flooded, roofs leaked, and water bills were rising. Many people told me that at first, they did not want to listen to yet another white person babbling on about something unrelated to their concerns. At Fred's invitation, I gave short pitches at community meetings about the need to collect and reuse water. These pitches were well received because I tried to be as practical and real as possible, rather than act like some outsider looking to test out her idea or make a buck. I attended barbecues and church gatherings. It took two years to develop enough relationships to build trust with community members.

Mapping played a central role in the evolution of Living Waters of Larimer. Mapping provided a space where everyone, regardless of their class and race, could think and learn together over a variety of maps about the local geography, ecology, and society. As a process, mapping empowered all of the project's participants and facilitated relationships between citizens and professionals. It eliminated the information gap that keeps so many people disempowered. We are not talking rocket science when we talk about mapping—we are learning common-sense, accessible knowledge of our human geography. Many people see a topographic map and assume they'll never be able to read it. But we pulled out colored pencils and laid large sheets of tracing paper over our maps, and invited everyone to think outside the box and begin to draw. Teams of three or four were formed and people with specific skills (art/design experience, landscape work) were distributed into different groups.

Mapping workshop

A diversity of disciplines is a great addition to any creative process. Christine Mondor from EvolveEA, an ecological landscape architecture firm, sent a person from her office, and some landscape design students from the local universities joined us. We made lists of priorities and learned where the waters flowed. Up until this point, no one even considered the possibility that the pipe system was something we could choose to change. The first mapping meeting went slowly and awkwardly. Participants were afraid to be the first to make their mark on the tracing paper. But people loosened up and by the end of the two-hour meeting, we were having a lively discussion. From then on, each progressive meeting produced more and more ideas. We used Geographic Information Systems (GIS) created by Land Base Systems to process mapping information in an intuitive way. Everybody could understand where runoff would naturally flow, where we could collect it, and where we could build cisterns to store it. One idea that arose was to mitigate localized flooding by capturing rainwater and diverting it to the wetlands before it hit the main boulevard. Another idea was inspired by ancient windmill systems: to create a stream along descending sidewalk steps that could generate electricity using a small turbine. Everyone in the group owned these ideas equally—which was essential.

Mapping workshop in Larimer

Possibilities sprung up: *We want this street to change. How about a greenway passing through our neighborhood? Could we bring this stream back to life?* Capturing this sort of excitement made it possible for us to fulfill all of the requirements of the public hearing stage. A community member installed her own rain barrel and discovered from her calculations that she had lowered her water bill by 60%. She went on to successfully teach others. All the ideas were generated by people with no particular "expertise," who came to the table to map and share their visions, and each step felt triumphant.

Over time, all participants were thinking outside the box, envisioning creating dead-end streets for young people to play, a waterway through the neighborhood, a centrally located cistern, and a park. We brainstormed businesses that could be formed from collecting the water, such as street cleaning, car washing, and papermaking. At one place where the water tumbled over a cliff, a community resident recognized the potential for a waterfall that could generate electricity.

All voices, ages, and experience levels were welcome at the table, and no plan was presented from the outside. All the ideas were generated by those who came to the workshops to map and learn. An eco-center, which had been built before we started but had little programming, became a focus of events and demonstrations. The plan was designed for the maximum collection of runoff in the community, complete with the optimum locations to place cisterns, a potential urban farm, bioswales, and income sources attached to the water collection.

Weekly dinners at a local Chinese restaurant became the most valuable time we all spent together. This became part of our budget meeting. It was especially useful for community members to get some relaxing time together away from their stressful and hectic lives. Slowly the white men involved in the project began to join in these dinners.

We applied for a Heinz Foundation grant to do a feasibility study—EvolveEA had the basics and understood what was needed. New challenges arose: the inevitable friction of an outside team, who gets paid, and for what? Some people had professional titles, and others did not. I insisted that all skills were equally important. It is essential to recognize this and to break through the strong barriers that keep us all in our own boxes. Foundations often inadvertently aggravate these differences. After months of deliberating on how to value the community members' time, we agreed that we'd gone through enough debate: everyone should get paid, no contracts were needed beyond a form for tracking hours—and we were done!

Who talks to whom, and who has access to money and control become invisible walls that maintain racism and classism. But those walls can come down, and they must. They are not immutable.

Larimer community meeting

An overarching issue in the project was the question of who had control of what. Regardless of what the community itself had planned, they had little control over what would happen in the end because they did not "own" the land. The city of Pittsburgh owned 60% of the land. This community chose a design company to design the new housing with HUD funding. The company was compatible with their vision, but they were not allowed to hire them. HUD functions under traditional models of economic development. It implements cookie-cutter housing, which does not prioritize community empowerment or sustainable design like rainwater collection, and is never integrated with local factors like sun direction or weather. We did the math and figured out that housing built with energy-saving materials would have paid for itself in five years. But working with HUD money, and facing a HUD team that would not budge, the community had to accept less-than-ideal designs.

We conceptualized The Well project. Our mapping process revealed to us the perfect location for this system: three vacant lots in central Larimer through which much runoff flowed, complete with plenty of space for a wetlands cleaning system. EvolveEA brought to the table visual ways for everyone in the room to sort out how to think about a site's assets and challenges. Their process helped clarify site candidates and eventually led us to our decision of what site would be best for The Well.

Carolyn Peeks (head of the Larimer Green Team) and I were hanging out, and she asked if the cistern could take the form of a tree. Wow! What an idea! How exciting to imagine a tree that drew water from the ground and captured water from the sky! This could be the center of a playground in which young people played. Water could flow from limbs or down roots. This was all to be designed by twelve community members, ages 16 to 80. Local Black artists in the community would design and make the artwork, tiles, and the stories of places embedded in the walls and the walkways. We won a large ArtPlace grant and identified foundations interested in adding to this funding.

Due to local politics, classism, racism, and a betrayal, this project was not executed. The funds were siphoned off for other uses. We were all devastated, but the project inspired similar actions in nearby communities. Along the way, we educated and inspired many, including people in local government.

This experience, along with many other experiences with communities, prompted me to share what I have learned. Caring for our waters is not rocket science. The science involved is generally already in a community or the institutions nearby. It requires a paradigm shift, which normalizes equity in the system and reflects the fact that all life is equally important.

Beijing Olympic Forest Park

The words of Yu Guang Yuan—economist and primary consul-
tant to Deng Xiaoping—stayed in my brain. He had told me that
I must work in Beijing because everything evolves from Beijing. I
returned to Beijing after my father died in 2000. Yu Guang Yuan
found me a position in the Beijing Bureau of Hydraulic Engineering
and Research, where I was to teach sustainable design.

I was welcomed by Cosima Liu, a woman who had just kayaked
through the inner-city waters of Beijing, Soon after arriving, I was
invited to a fundraiser, where Jane Goodall spoke. After her talk,
she was asked by a businessman about the cost of implementing
environmental practices. She lowered her head slightly, thought for
a moment, and then replied with a light tone in her voice. "This
is all about greed, isn't it?" Once I settled into Beijing I joined the
Board of the Jane Goodall Institute. I watched Jane, traveled with
her, and learned some of the biggest lessons of my life. Do not
blame or scold people, just meet people where they are and invite
them to think about how to start. At the end of a long day we
would gather for a glass of wine while Jane put her feet up and we
all relaxed. Although I worked on many interesting and challenging
projects, looking back it is clear to me that watching Jane gave me
something intangible and immeasurable. If you ask me what it was,
I find it hard to express. I experienced a woman who walks in the
world with integrity, a woman who respects all life and expects the
best from people while never compromising herself. She listens to
all and encourages people's innate desire to do their best.

I quickly learned that most people in the Water Bureau and in
landscape design companies would design based on theory or mag-
azines. We began by visiting each river or site and walking around.
Learning with my feet—feeling the land—is a basic step for me. We
drafted solutions and sustainable designs. After walking the river,
sometimes for miles, I would meet with the Beijing planning bureau.
I asked to look at maps. Ironically, they very few maps to look at.

They had rarely thought about where the waters came from or how they flowed through the land. Restoration and development were planned with no regard for water capacity or flow.

The Beijing Water Bureau took me to historic water sites, such as fields where the best rice had been grown for the emperor. I learned the history of Beijing's water supplies. This water grew the sweetest rice for the empress, or these hot springs were a favorite place to go. Rivers trickled through the eastern mountains. Haidian, a place of ten thousand springs on the west side of Beijing, had supplied Beijing's water for centuries. Haidian now sprouts high-rise buildings and commercial complexes. Beijing has very little rain, but had a supply of groundwater that was beginning to rapidly deplete. The machinery of development to prepare for the Olympics in Beijing took over. Regardless of the realities of the water situation, the motto became *develop, develop, develop.*

At the beginning of my time there, I attended several high-level meetings about the water crisis in Beijing. Residents were saving shower water for their toilets. Beijing's water infrastructure lost 30% of its daily capacity to leaks. A proposal was on the table to replace all toilets with new low-use models, and freely repair interior leaks. All of this was suddenly buried, however, as Beijing began construction for the 2008 Olympic Games. All these good ideas were abandoned to create an illusion of an infinite water supply.

Over the next eight years, I witnessed the elimination of historic sites and the transformation of the big, beautiful, old tree-lined rivers into concrete ditches. On our weekly picnics in the hills, we found that all the small streams had dried up. The Water Bureau had proudly tried to capture every drop of water that fell on the hills, so now the peasants no longer had water for their crops. The huge plan to divert water from the south to the north began to deliver water, which was then pumped into the north to be returned to Beijing. All of this was regarded as progress. How long will this infrastructure last? The Beijing Water Bureau partially took up my proposed changes for the murky, constricted rivers of the city. The designers generated many creative designs for cleaning water, including placing wetlands and waterfalls along the edges of an old river. In doing this, a flow was created by pumping water up, and spilling it back through elaborate waterfalls where rivers' walls became cleaning gabions.[25]

After 2008, one Water Bureau designer proudly showed me how he had placed a wetland structure on top of concrete side-walls, cleaning the river enough that fishing returned. He had asked the Water Corps if he could try it, and told them that if it did not work, then it would be taken out. This small portion of a vast Beijing water network gives hope that more and more innovations will eventually come. The Beijing Planning Bureau asked that I write guidelines for integrating ecological systems into planning and design. They invited me to assemble the teams to design projects with Chinese landscape companies. Each one of these projects won awards for sustainability.

Tertiary cleaning in a greenhouse

At my invitation, Margot Young, CEO of Environmental Design and Management Canada, joined a team competing for the Wen Yu River and the Olympic Forest Park projects. We created the water plan for the entire Olympic site which connected all the waters. Water beginning in a greenhouse cleaning system would flow to collect oxygen and settle into wetlands for cleaning and move throughout the entire site. The plan included a greenhouse treatment of water from a large wastewater treatment plant, and proposed to supply the entire site with healthy water—with a surplus—at minimal expense. This plan addressed Beijing's critical water scarcity. Our plan would have implemented a real model of connectivity that would have ensured a living system throughout the Olympic areas. But this plan was eventually rejected because the two districts that controlled the site could not agree. The district that stood to make the most money off the project rejected any collaboration or coordination to ensure a connected system. Although I pleaded with the engineers to make sure that all the parts were connected, they disconnected each section from the next. Water was re-circulated within each section, causing toxins to accumulate.

Mapping Tibetan Water Culture

After five years in Beijing, I found myself longing to return to the *God* Water. The 2008 Beijing Olympics were approaching, and almost every transitional water site had been destroyed to make room for high rises and Olympic training sites. I was constantly preoccupied with what had happened to those waters. Was the extensive culture that had protected the upland waters in Western Sichuan for thousands of years still there? Or was it being rapidly destroyed by mining and extraction, as were similar places in the world? Maybe I was missing those people who put water as the

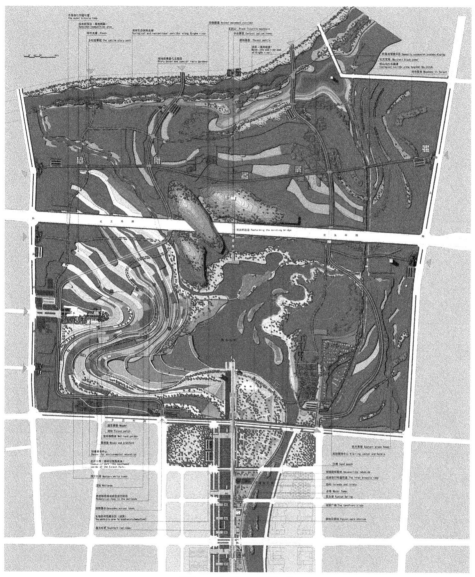

Olympic Forest Park

foundation, who knew their waters. Part of me wanted to give up exhausting myself on projects.

In 2006, I found a short time to travel from Beijing to Chengdu. A new road to Songpan made the trip an easy eight hours. To my delight, I found that the area of the *God* Water had been made into a national park. The road into the bottling factory was nearly invisible as we wound our way up the mountain. Unable to drive up close, we parked our car and walked, only to find the factory in ruins. The remains of the housing were still there, but the barbed wire that surrounded the spring was gone. To our surprise, as we climbed the stairs to the rooms where we had stayed, we met a caretaker who remembered me. We sat together, drank tea, and chatted for a long time. The caretaker said that people were still coming to fetch the water, and he shared how they had won back the land from the Chinese business people.

The visit to the *God* Water was exactly what I needed—a place that was animated by water and where the pulse of life could be felt.

This was a glimpse into the water culture in western Sichuan, home to many Tibetan tribal cultures. The following year. I was able to organize another short trip. Once again people discouraged me, warning me that I wouldn't find anything, and claiming that no one would talk to me because I was a white woman with a Chinese guide. My intuition was confirmed on an eight-day exploration with Tang Ya, a guide, and Brenda Hood, a Beijing friend who had studied Taoist esoteric practices. My son told me about an innkeeper named Jo Ma in Ba Mei, and suggested I speak with her. Sure enough, she happily told us, "Right down the road is a temple with sacred water. I will go with you." We set off on foot, and as we walked, she told the story of the temple. A lama threw three stones: one found the water, one landed at the site of the village, and the third landed at the place for the temple.

When we came to the temple, I dutifully followed her instructions—first placing my head three times under the stream of freezing water; next sipping the water three times and spitting it out after each sip; then three swallows of water. Nearby, a large scarred tree was decorated with prayer flags. The story of this tree was that during the Cultural Revolution, the Red Guards set it on fire. When it

Area around the God Water

Meeting at the God Water

Sacred Tree of Ba Mei Temple

would not burn, they tried to cut it down. When they tried to cut it down, the tree bled, so they fled in fear. Afterward, we all walked through the meadows picking wild strawberries, Jo Ma happily identifying various edibles.

The following day, Jo Ma directed us to two more sites in the area. One of these was the Butter Water, an amazingly sweet water that seeped from the base of a mountain on which the locals gathered herbs and wild mushrooms. The story of this water was that it saved the life of a starving woman, who was journeying on foot to her next master. Her three-year-old son was with her, saw that she was weak and starving, and asked her to drink the water. She replied, "Do not be stupid. It will not make me strong." But he begged her, and she drank. The water gave her enough strength to finish their journey. Sure enough, after we drank from the Butter Water, our stomachs felt full. This water is the best water in the area and is vigorously protected.

The following year, in 2008, I went back to Chengdu, hoping to research the sacred sites further. However, with many apologies and a good meal, the director of foreign travelers told me that regrettably I was not allowed to travel, because of a terrible earthquake that had recently killed over 87,000 people. Understandably, the roads were impassable and mudslides presented a constant threat. Instead, I raised money for a volunteer group called Yak Train that was taking the bare necessities to villagers who had lost everything.

One evening I wandered into a Tibetan-owned store called Kalu across the street from my hotel, and was invited to drink barley tea with the owner, Lhacuo Zhaxi. We fell into conversation, and as it happened, Lhacuo was a documentary filmmaker who was documenting Tibetan culture but had never before heard of the water sites. Three meetings later, I gave her the three thousand dollars I had saved for the trip to research the water cultures. Lhacuo discovered that her mother knew many sites, and together they visited eight sites. This began a six-year collaboration to document the water culture of the tribes in Western Sichuan.

Between 2007 and 2013, Lhacuo and I traveled on five-month-long trips, documenting the water-based cultures in Western Sichuan. We visited over forty different water sites, and documented an extensive culture of honoring and conserving water. Flags and signs carved into stones or a small temple marked many sites as

Betsy taking in the waters

Site of the Butter Water

those conserved for drinking. They knew that forests ensured that springs would exist. Often villagers were forbidden to cut the forests behind their villages. Herd animals were forbidden near headwaters with the injunction that if you grazed your yak near those waters, the yaks would all die. This might sound odd, but this was analogous to a hundred-thousand-dollar fine for polluting. Every place had similar injunctions: do not wash your hands here or you and your relatives will get arthritis; or a drop of your blood falling into the water ensures an illness for you. They were keepers of their resources, and the collateral was a human body or the yaks. There is no doubt about the value placed on water in these villages. Forests are managed to protect the waters, and drinking water is carefully protected and kept separate from the water used for farming and animals. However, each year we returned, we found that more and more villages were losing their waters, as hydroelectric dams were built upstream and extraction industries moved further and further into rural areas. These sites, which have supported communities for thousands of years, are rapidly disappearing due to urban expansion, extraction, and globalization.

Traveling by motorcycle to a remote water site

Here are two of the forty adventures we had. In 2009, I had raised just enough funding to return to Chengdu with Brock

Dolman, the Water Director at the Occidental Art and Ecology Center in Occidental, CA. We set out on a month-long trip. Our first stop was Muli Monastery, a large monastery in southern Sichuan. Winding up a dirt road, we stopped briefly at a small temple structure from which water gushed into a roaring stream. We ascended another mile and turned a corner to arrive at a large monastery. Immediately, the head monk stepped out and invited us in for tea and snacks. After the greetings and a welcoming tea, we awkwardly tried to make conversation. I asked if we could clean up the trash in the stream at the temple. Grinning, the head monk said that he would give us his students for the day. He told us that after the Cultural Revolution, the stream had run dry. I asked how the water had returned. "Was it prayer?" I asked with a smile. With a twinkle in his eyes, he said that they had replanted the forest. He understood the intimate connection between the forest and the rivers: that trees capture, hold, and release water.

Monks cleaning the river

The next morning, our team and about thirty students from the monastery ran down to the stream, where the monks began picking up sticks and dead leaves. They did not know what was garbage, or that the plastic would not disappear, because in the past everything was biodegradable. When I explained what garbage actually was, they spent the next five hours cleaning every tire, cement bag, plastic bottle, and other non-degradable pieces of garbage out of the river. We arranged a truck to carry the garbage down the mountain to be recycled. Additionally, it would have been exciting to create a wastewater system in a greenhouse that would compost and heat to grow greens.

Badalama Cave

The Badalama River is a major tributary of the Yangtze, running high in the mountains. The area around it and the forests below it are protected. To reach the river, we spent a night in a village and hired people from the village to take us up to the source on horseback several hours through farmland up into the mountains. At one point, after about three hours, we stopped and our guides performed a ritual before we could go up into the cave. The ceremony was to burn cedar, say prayers, and hang flags. From that point on, the climb was so steep that we walked, leaving the horses behind.

Badalama Cave

Out of breath, we arrived at the headwaters of the river. It's hard to describe how extraordinarily alive and powerful this site is. It takes time to be with the waters, to absorb the air, and notice an environment so alive. People honored the cave by leaving prayer flags, bits of cloth, and trinkets. We found our way deep into the cave where we experimented with lights and flashlights. While we explored, our guides sourced wild mushrooms and other edibles to prepare lunch.

Outside the cave the water pours through rocks and lush vegetation. You can stand and breathe in the ions from the water. We spent a couple of hours in that environment before finding our way back. The forest below the cave is protected and no one is allowed to source the syrup from the trees without a special permit. The farmland below is noticeably healthy. I was looking at all the ways the farmers had devised to distribute the water fairly. They had developed multiple methods of protection.

Badalama vegetation

This was the last trip in 2013. My son Jon told me of the incredible beauty of Yalu Mountain. We could not go for many years because the local people were protesting a gold mining company that wanted to mine the mountain. When it was finally possible to travel, I asked Jo Ma, the inn manager, to arrange a guide and horses for the five of us to go up to 14,000 feet and camp. One night, sitting around a fire, we discovered that our guide was the leader of the protests that had taken place. He told us the story of how every farmer in the valley refused to farm for five years. I know the valley he spoke of: the Butter Water, which we documented, supported the health of the villagers. It was a clean and clearly prosperous place. The farmers petitioned Beijing over and over again to preserve this sacred mountain. Some people even went to jail. But in the end, they won, and the mining company withdrew.

These trips revitalized me, but more importantly, we created documentation of an undocumented culture that sustained the Himalayan/Tibetan tribes. Every place has a way to protect its waters and many places were being destroyed primarily by the rapid damming of all major rivers. The villagers were losing their waters, and along with them a way of life. Although change is inevitable, the damming of rivers needs to be considered more carefully. There is no inherent conflict between development and preserving waters, but overzealous damming is destructive. The waters held behind a dam heat up, flows are destroyed, the impact on people and wildlife is incalculable.

FINDING YOUR WATER BALANCE

Having mapped your community's water, now you can think about your community's water usage footprint. Rarely do citizens know their water balance.

There is only so much water available for use at any given time, and choices need to be made about how it is used. Knowing your available water can determine how you plan and build. Do you need low-use toilets? Do you need to capture rainwater to repurpose? We can think of the water available for use like a water bank account, which needs to be kept in balance. Plenty of water is coming into the bank account—rainfall, flowing streams and rivers, and wells drilled into aquifers. Water is "spent" when we displace it or make it dirty. If the expenditures are larger than the amount coming in, there will be a water

"deficit." The deficit may be local (e.g., your lake, river or reservoir is being depleted) or you may be borrowing from some other community that may or may not be able to spare it.

Borrowing water negatively impacts the lender's ecosystem. Even if it appears that the lender has a lot of water, borrowing is a temporary solution. Typically, because of our enormous demand for water, we extract more water for use than is sustainable, resulting in lower water tables or lake levels. In some places, these issues are reaching crisis conditions.

Creating a consciousness about your water balance would enable the community as a whole to make good decisions about source

and uses of water. For example, drinking water is often used to clean streets, which is a complete waste. Our streets could be cleaned with rainwater, or effluent from a wastewater treatment plant. Wise water use needs to be a collective, community decision, and that can only be made when we have knowledge.

A great example of borrowing is Mono Lake, north of Los Angeles. It was the main source of water for Los Angeles for fifty years. Mono Lake was heavily depleted and its surrounding ecosystem damaged. A restoration of Mono Lake is underway, thanks to the Mono Lake Committee. This committee "works to restore the ecological functions of Mono Lake, its tributary streams and waterfowl habitat, and the watershed as a whole."[26] The Mono Lake Committee is grounded in restoring water balance: it was formed after the State Water Board listened to community concerns and voted unanimously to "figure out precisely how much water was needed in order to protect the ecological resources."

Your water balance can be calculated by finding out how much rainfall you receive and how much water can reasonably be drawn from nearby waterways.

The following diagram illustrates three processes to consider when thinking about Water Balance. They are Precipitation, Flow-through Water, and Off-site Water.

If this is mysterious to you, find someone in your community who can explain water balance to you. In my forty years of working with water, I only learned about water balance recently.

Precipitation is water that falls from the sky into our community, in the form of rain, snow, and fog drip. Precipitation follows three primary pathways once it falls: up, down, and off. It is returned to the sky (up) through evapo-transpiration (used by trees and other vegetation) or evaporation into the air. Or it is added to what we term *through water*—water flowing through a community—either as surface water if the precipitation runs off surfaces into inlets (off), or as groundwater if the precipitation soaks into the ground (down). Base maps illustrate the different surfaces in our community and allow us to consider both how much precipitation is likely to follow each pathway and the types of contaminants it is likely to come into contact with as it flows.

Through water includes both surface water (concentrated flow along the surface in both watercourses and piped systems) and ground-water. I find it helpful to imagine these systems as moving flows that are passing through a community. What right do you have to take through water? What does damming do to the flow of the water?

Surface Water

As precipitation falls on the surfaces in our community, it initially moves as sheet flow, or a broad movement across a surface. At some point, it begins to move as a concentrated flow, where it begins to act like a stream of water. On your roof, this starts to happen in the gutter and downspout; on the street, it begins along the edge curb and the catch basin inlet; in a natural stream, it begins as rivulets that make their way to streams and rivers. Surface water–through water maps include all elements of surface water. Water courses are defined as all-natural water bodies that convey concentrated flow, including wetlands, brooks, streams and lakes. In urban environments, piped stormwater systems have replaced segments of water courses, and are included on the surface water–through water map.

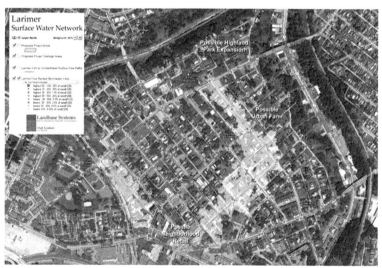

Larimer surface water map

Stormwater

Stormwater is a big issue, particularly due to the vast sprawl of cities. Typically, the water that passes over roads and parking lots, urban areas, and rural roadways, is captured in pipes, and sent directly into our rivers. Draining our hard surfaces with perceived excess rainfall has created many problems. First, when the water comes from a heavily traveled road, it contains particulate matter such as dust and unburned fuel. These contaminants pollute the river that receives the stormwater. Second, the ground surrounding roads needs water to support plant life, and plants filter that water. Roadside drainage pipes deprive the roadside landscape of the water it needs. Last, sending water through pipes straight into streams brings too much water into streams, which then flood and suffer from erosion problems. Roads are one of the biggest threats to ecosystems because they interrupt flow. Watch what happens on your driveway or street after a rainstorm.

The word *stormwater* implies that we need pipes, and that there is something wrong with that water. But are pipes always the solution? Instead, I prefer to call stormwater "rainwater" and talk about repurposing it. Rainwater should be captured and repurposed everywhere. This water can be used to clean roads, or by various businesses. Rainwater is a good source of clean water. People ask if the water is really clean—what about the dirty air the rain falls through? Yes, there can be pollutants from factories that land on surfaces like roofs, glass, roads etc. This air pollution needs to stop. The rainwater that

falls on a roof also washes the roof, removing pollutants. This is called "first flush"—the first rain to fall on a roof will contain pollutants if you are capturing rainwater, but the subsequent water captured from that roof will be clean. If you can create a natural filtering system of sand and gravel for your rainwater, then you can use it safely. If there are doubts about the quality, then boil the water for cooking and drinking. It is likely that rainwater will become a primary source for clean water in the future. Our watersheds have been

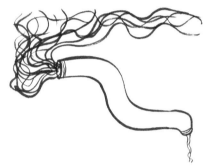

fragmented and largely turned into pipeshed. We waste water almost everywhere, including places where water is scarce. Some water transfer systems are famous, like in Los Angeles or Las Vegas. But these places employ few practices to save water.

"This crucial movement of water needs to be recognized for what it is—a fundamental creative force."
—JOHN WILKES

Groundwater

Groundwater is often a significant water source. Groundwater mainly collects in aquifers, deep-moving bodies of water under the ground. It can be easy to forget groundwater, especially as the amount of impervious surface area, like sidewalks and roads, increases in our communities. In calculating a water balance, we are considering the shallow groundwater system that is moving at or near the surface in our communities and interacting at times with the surface water system. Some communities also have very deep groundwater sources or deep aquifers that generally do not interact with the community, unless they have been tapped with wells to use them as a drinking water source or a source of irrigation. Where this is the case, we consider this "borrowing" water because an aquifer doesn't recharge on its own. In other words, the aquifer isn't part of your bank account because it is shared.

Borrowed Water

Money does not replace water

90% of LA's water comes from elsewhere

Borrowed water is any outside water source that we bring to our community via pipeline or river, usually for drinking water. This includes precipitation that has fallen somewhere else that we have appropriated from another community for our own use. Because we don't send used water back to the source community, we are creating an imbalance in their system.

Maps and information are organized by agencies and professions according to categories that are useful to them. Their maps are often specific to the jobs they are doing. For example, there are separate maps for pipes, and the pipes may not correspond to the landforms. If you are looking to understand a larger picture, you need landform maps and pipe system maps together.

Calculating the Water Budget

You need to do a bit of math for this. The numbers may surprise you, and your conclusions will be valuable in deciding what actions to take to benefit your watershed. This may be the perfect job for someone who likes math, but anyone can do it.

Using your maps, you can estimate the amounts of different types of land areas in your community or your watershed. A general estimate is that half of the land of a city is made up of impervious surfaces like roads, sidewalks and other pavement. Different surfaces receive water differently: most hard surfaces (rooftops, concrete, asphalt, etc.) are largely impervious, meaning that they do not suck up water or allow water to flow through them. Precipitation falling on these surfaces will run off heading downhill. Lawns are barely permeable; they are one step away from concrete. How much of your community's surface area is forested?

On the other hand, permeable areas permit far less runoff, as they allow more water to soak into the ground. As in impervious surfaces, actual behavior will vary with many factors, including surface type, slope, soil compaction and groundwater levels, and will also vary with each storm.

To put these words into numbers, you can assign different numbers, called **runoff coefficients**, to different land types. **Runoff coefficients always fall between zero and one (between zero and 100% of precipitation runs off).** Look at the following table:

Ground Cover	Runoff Coefficient, c
Lawns	0.2 (0.05−0.35)
Forest	0.15 (0.05−0.25)
Cultivated land	0.25 (0.08-0.41)
Meadow	0.3 (0.1−0.5)
Parks, cemeteries	0.18 (0.1−0.25)
Unimproved areas	0.2 (0.1−0.3)
Pasture	0.37 (0.12−0.62)
Residential areas	0.53 (0.3−0.75)
Business areas	0.73 (0.5−0.95)
Industrial areas	0.7 (0.5−0.9)
Asphalt streets	0.83 (0.7−0.95)
Brick streets	0.78 (0.7−0.85)
Roofs	0.85 (0.75−0.95)
Concrete streets	0.83 (0.7−0.95)

The range of coefficients for, say, different types of roofs appears in parentheses next to the average coefficient. Impervious surfaces, such as streets, have coefficients closer to one—this is because nearly all of the water runs off (1 = 100%). Forests, however, only run off five to 25% of rainfall.

So you've estimated the different surface types and their areas for your community. Here's the math:[27]

(Imagine your community has 25% forested areas, 50% roofs and asphalt streets, and 25% cultivated farmland)

1. Multiply the percent area by the appropriate coefficient from the table above:

    0.25 (25% forested area) x 0.15 (runoff coefficient for forest) = 0.0375

    0.5 (50% roofs and asphalt streets) x 0.85 (roofs coefficient) = 0.425

    0.25 (25% farmland) x 0.25 (cultivated land coefficient) = 0.0625

These numbers represent the amount of rainfall that runs off in your community per land type. So, altogether they will represent your whole community.

2. Add the results together:

$$0.0375 + 0.425 + 0.0625 = 0.525$$

This means that about 52.5% of water that falls on your community runs off into streams, rivers, lakes and storm drains.

Hopefully, you have seen some historical maps. It is possible that your community used to have 50% forested areas, 30% cultivated farmland, 10% pasture, and 10% roofs. Let's quickly do the math and see what it was like when it rained back then:

$$0.5 \times 0.15 = 0.075 \qquad \text{(Forests)}$$
$$0.3 \times 0.25 = 0.075 \qquad \text{(Farms)}$$
$$0.1 \times 0.37 = 0.037 \qquad \text{(Pastures)}$$
$$0.1 \times 0.85 = 0.085 \qquad \text{(Roofs)}$$

$$0.075 + 0.075 + 0.037 + 0.085 = 0.272$$

In this example, 27.2% of the rain ran off. That means that a community with fewer asphalt surfaces and more green areas can have *twice* as much water in its bank account.

You can play with these numbers to imagine how much water you would save by imagining different materials and designs for your roads, parks, and roofs. For more accurate and detailed numbers, you will have to consult engineers or put in more time for research. Calculating your water budget allows you to begin to make important design decisions.

Water Balance in Action: Chinook Bend

Another opportunity arose in 2004 when I participated in 4Culture's competition for a public art piece for the Chinook Bend Natural Area in Carnation, Washington. King County Wastewater Treatment Division set aside a portion of their budget for art generated by a new wastewater treatment plant in Carnation—the place where the dairy that made Carnation Evaporated Milk was founded. I was delighted to be chosen by 4Culture as the artist for Chinook Bend Natural Area. The wastewater treatment plant's effluent was to be used to enhance a pond and wetland area. I sought to reveal, celebrate, and honor the fifty-eight acres of a restored natural area located next to one of the last pristine salmon spawning rivers in America.

I met with all the parties involved: Carnation citizens, members of the Snoqualmie Tribe (who had just received federal recognition), numerous departments from King County, and Ducks Unlimited, a wetlands and waterfowl conservation organization. While we were in the process of getting to know each other, King County Wastewater made an unusual decision. They decided to remove the flood control berms to provide optimal conditions for salmon. This was a first. Perhaps my insistence on meeting with so many different people sparked this decision, especially given the resistance to seasonal flooding among the local farmers. In response to the removal of flood control berms to allow seasonal flooding at the site, I designed a glass and granite measuring pole which looked like a spine, to measure the flooding. This is accompanied by a large granite compass for people to sit on, and some seating stones made from glacial boulders. Today, people enjoy seeing how high the flooding reaches on the measuring pole. Seasonal flooding has begun to restore the ecosystem's complexity and resilience, and allowed the river to carve itself more space to freely flow and support all the life within it.

Control and Ownership

Pole to measure floods in Chinook Bend Natural Area

Every country has different rules and regulations. In the U.S., water regulations vary greatly from state to state. Along the way, you will find out who controls your water and discover the people and groups that will be integral members of your coalition.

Responsibility for different aspects of our water systems has been divided up. This has led to not only the fragmentation of our waters, but also social, economic and political obstacles to re-connecting our waters.

In the United States, the Army Corps of Engineers retains control over most large waterways. The government and hydroelectric firms control most dams. Groundwater is not well controlled, and companies can buy and exploit the water in aquifers and springs, sometimes merely by buying the land above. In the United States, any company can buy up the rights to freshwater supplies. Water rights in the Western United States are a boondoggle, creating a mass of issues that can make it challenging to cooperate around bodies of water.

Here are some of the institutions and groups that exert control over water:

Federal Government: It enforces laws related to water and environmental health, such as the Clean Water Act and the Endangered Species Act.

Big Businesses: More and more companies are buying water resources as investments and for resource extraction. This puts these water resources under private control.

Farmers: In many states, water rights are maintained by seniority and land ownership. In the Western United States, this means that many agricultural industries control the water. Farmers are implementing better techniques for using less water more efficiently.

State Governments: These control water rights and distribution in a state. Each state has different water laws and regulations to account for their different climates and industries. Some states outlaw diversion of rainwater, even to the extent that their citizens cannot install rain barrels on their properties.

Cities: Cities buy water rights from adjoining areas to provide for their citizens. Sometimes these water sources are far away from the city. For example, Los Angeles imports 85% of its drinking water. Residents in cities have argued that they are entitled to a "reasonable residential experience." This experience includes golf courses, lawns, and parks, straining the water resources both locally and at a distance where the water is sourced.

People with Money: When water is treated as a consumer good, access to it is rooted in the consumer's ability to pay. Without a social consciousness of the right of life for all people, water becomes a resource that the wealthy can have and those who cannot pay cannot have. During the 2015 drought in California, residents in some poorer neighborhoods were fined for extraneous uses of water. Meanwhile, in wealthier neighbor-hoods, many homeowners did little to curb water usage. One resident, known as the "Wet Prince" of Bel Air, used the same amount of water as ninety typical California families.

Homeowners: If you own a piece of property, you may assume you own the water on it. This does not always prove to be true. In Colorado, it was illegal to collect rainwater from your own property until 2016. Increasingly, municipalities are trying to own all the water. In some places in Pennsylvania, for example, the water authority ripped out privately built rain barrels.

In Flint, Michigan in 2014, the city's water source was switched from Detroit's municipal system to the Flint River to cut costs. The Flint River water proved to be corrosive, leading to dangerously elevated levels of lead in the potable water supply. Who fixed those pipes, and whose responsibility was it? The local community did not have the resources to fix something that was not theirs to fix, and no government agency stepped up for more than two years. Now, years later, Flint's water is still in crisis. Delivering bottled water for years is not a solution. Flint faces many injustices, from decades of indus-trial dumping by General Motors and its suppliers, to ancient and corroded pipes, to the greed of those who are profiting off of water.

Future Generations: Up until 2016, farmers in California were allowed to pump unlimited amounts of groundwater, and they were extracting much faster than the water could recharge. If groundwater extraction is unregulated, we can look forward to a problematic and more difficult future. The Ogallala Aquifer, covering eight states in the Midwest, primarily contains fossil water—water that's been undisturbed for millennia— from the time of the last ice age. The Ogallala Aquifer supports a staggering one-sixth of the world's grain production.[28] The aquifer has long been unable to keep up with these agricultural demands, and is seriously depleted. Some states have had some level of success in slowing down the aquifer's depletion. Kansas, for example, has recently achieved mild success by adopting a program that puts conservation in the hands of the state's farmers.

The Environment: Water rights were intended to prioritize allocating water between humans. But we've forgotten that the rivers, lakes, and ecosystems need water. We've forgotten that water, by definition of its essential role, must be a shared resource. The Indigenous tribes of New Mexico would share their waters with each other in times of drought, ensuring that each could survive.

Control and ownership

The various overlaps of controlling agencies and individuals are a patchwork—municipal water is treated and conserved, but is delivered in two different ways: through public water and through bottled water (30% or more of which is drawn from the same water supply as your tap water).[29] Farmers and agricultural firms who work with soil are not brought into the wastewater treatment process, even though they could produce some of the best fertilizer available. Rivers are segmented by municipal boundaries, and by dams and their owners. Listening to each other might make it possible to solve some very sticky issues around water rights.

Owning water / owning the body

Water is the sustaining lifeblood of this planet. But we have cut it up and divided it. Imagine if we did this to ourselves, to our own circulatory system. At what point is the system so dismantled that it cannot thrive? We are dangerously close to that point.

Ogallala Aquifer
(source: Wikimedia Commons by Kbh3rd)

Single-Purpose Design

Water connects everything. Single-purpose design fails to acknowledge earth's interconnectedness, opting instead to solve problems on a shortsighted and piecemeal basis. Single-purpose design becomes evident when we address water. The notion of treating different water elements independently, as if they can be separated is a big contributor to the predicament that we find ourselves in now. Where did the idea of separating water systems come from? Separating our waters is like cutting off limbs of the body to exert control.

Rivers and Streams

A meandering stream that changes speed and direction, that passes under trees and occasionally underground, that animals drink from, and that humans draw from and replenish, *is*

alive. You can see that it is clean: organisms like mayflies, caddisflies, water pennies, and gilled snails thrive in its path.

Planners have straightened rivers for more convenient shipping, increased control, and to claim more land for farming or for cities. Now we've built so close to rivers that large walls are needed to hold the waters in, and in times of big rain events, the water often breaches those walls disastrously. The Mississippi, once a great, meandering river, moves less than half the sediment it once could.[30] The nutrient-rich soils that would be deposited by the river as it slowly descended into the delta are dredged up instead. These sediments created rich farmlands and built up the delta to protect New Orleans. This situation repeats itself in countless rivers around the world.

The capacity of rivers to hold water has also been reduced. Many big river systems can no longer respond flexibly to changes in their waters. The Bonnet Carré spillway, a major floodgate on the Mississippi River, is a telling example: "Over its first eighty years in operation, [it] was activated just ten times. Then something changed. The river hit the trigger point in 2011, 2016, 2018 and—for the first time ever in back-to-back years."[31] Rather than restore capacity in our rivers, we further disconnect small streams, making the problem worse and worse.

Then we have urban pipes and pumps for stormwater. The single purpose is to remove water. Pumps and pipes decay and break. The people who care for these systems are trained to use a very specific toolkit, and all they know is how to use that toolkit. They don't know how to adjust their designs to return the water to the land. Currently, stormwater is sent into pipes that dump the water straight into a river. No matter how large a pipe is, it never ends up being large enough, especially given the realities of climate change. The alternative is to create a flexible landscape that can respond to a wider range of precipitation.

All these systems are inherently interconnected. In recent times, estuaries and wetlands have been viewed as useless spaces ready for development. They have been protected by few regulations or conservation efforts—yet they are the nurseries of life on earth. Estuaries at the mouths of rivers have been converted almost exclusively into places for the shipping industry. The single purpose was to be able to receive cargo ships, to send goods out, and to receive goods in.

Concrete—what an invention! Let's put it on everything: roads, parking lots, driveways. Got a patch of dirt? Cover it in concrete.

Roads are universally designed where the edge is built up so that rainwater flows off into pipes before entering streams and rivers. But the best design for roads from a water standpoint is to let the water run off the side of the road and into the landscape. This requires road designs that respond to the curves and ups and downs of the road. It also requires a three-foot deep ditch filled with pebbles running alongside the road, which acts as a filtering system for dirty road runoff.

Wetlands and Estuaries

Wetlands are generally considered movable and a waste place. The eradication of wetlands is a direct result of not considering the interconnectedness of all systems.

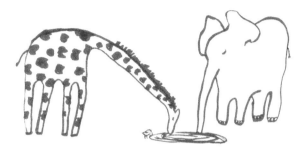

Where does that humming of springtime or the sudden voice of frogs in summer come from? Wetlands are incredible nurseries; so much life is created in wetlands. Most of the fish we eat, and nearly half of all threatened and endangered species, are reliant on wetland habitats.[32] One of our greatest offenses has been to see a wetland as a development site, without understanding the enormous value it holds to nurture life and regulate water movement.

Estuaries form the meeting point between fresh water and the ocean, and are some of the largest wetlands and nurseries we have. Not only are they vital to the food chain, but they also are critical in filtering water of impurities and imbalances, and responding flexibly to mitigate variations in water levels. Coastal wetlands can help in mitigating rising waters. Cities like Boston[33] are waking up to the reality of climate chaos and are creating plans to augment their coastal wetlands and expand their capacities.

The importance of these functions has been underestimated. Historically, and some might say logically, estuaries have been converted to harbors for shipping. An example from right in my backyard is the Gowanus Canal in Brooklyn, which was once a fresh water-salt water estuary. Builders recently created high-rise apartments butting almost to the edge of the water. Everything is encased in concrete, and no wild growth to absorb the waters was allowed. Such planning is shortsighted; future flooding problems have been ensured. Estuaries are natural filters for runoff, and can help regions adjust to changes in sea levels. Given the increasing speed of changes coming, we desperately need them.

Since 1900, 64% (some estimates are as high as 70%) of global wetland area has disappeared, and even more has degraded.[34] The trend has not yet leveled off. Steady losses of global wetland areas deprive ecosystems of life, natural filtration systems, flood control, groundwater recharge, and carbon sequestration. Wetlands are complexity at work. The economic benefits of wetlands on a global scale have been estimated to be worth over a hundred trillion dollars annually[35] (more than five times the GDP of the United States in 2016). Wetlands are being bulldozed for development, purportedly for economic reasons. The recent loss of wetlands may amount to between four and twenty trillion dollars.[36] Not only does the trend of wetland loss need to be abated; it must be reversed to recover these valuable and complex systems. These are essential for the future of all living systems.

Bioindicators

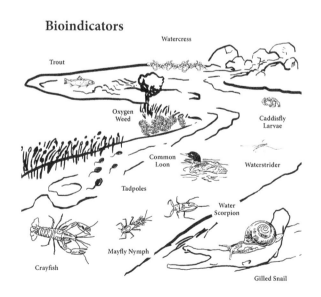

Curitiba, Brazil is an interesting city that left the space for their river to flood. This space doubles as parkland and provides an area for the river to flood without destroying housing. They did not build to the edge of the river. Most of the conversations that I've participated in focus on forcing the river to adjust to the city; not asking how a city can give space for the river to run and flood. Do you force a river to adjust to the city? Or how do you adjust the city to the river?

Headwaters

The best water goes up and down
the mountain ten thousand times.
—ANCIENT CHINESE WISDOM

Very few of us live near headwaters—they're distant, often high up in the mountains. Large ecosystems depend on the vitality of these waters. Each headwaters has its particular energy. The Mississippi River bubbles up in the meadow—the multiple harmonies of the meadow are amazing to hear. The Yangtze River pours out of a glacier at more than 17,000 feet, crashing into the rocks and traveling through glacial moraines, flowing thunderously down gorges, and then through farmland toward the Pacific. The Badalama, a large river that feeds the Yangtze, emerges from a cave, creating a place so green that our guides prepared our lunch from the plants and mushrooms that they found along it. I have asked if there is a study researching the impact on life of the degrading of these waters. As far as I know, there is no such study. Yet it must be that the wildlife and particular living forms that evolved along each river are dependent on the characteristics of that water. These upland waters are often protected by the Indigenous people who rely on them. Their waters are being gobbled up by extraction, mining, and consumption by cities. It is time to join with them to protect these sources.

Extraction: Oil, Mining, Fracking, and Water

The devastation wreaked upon the waters by extractive industries must be exposed and heavily regulated. We are aware of oil spills and the enormous efforts to clean them up. Mines harvesting copper, coal, gold, and other precious metals ravage the ecosystem, filling rivers with shale and other detritus from excavation. Mineral mining around the world uses a large number of highly toxic chemicals. Large areas have been utterly decimated by mining, destroyed for the foreseeable future. Recognition of the enormous problems created by mining is spawning an effort toward sustainable mining. The waters left in large holes from copper mines are so toxic that, as far as I know, no one has figured out what to do, and we seem to be relying on luck to control the potential disasters that could occur when these waters overflow out of their pits. I jokingly proposed that we dump masses of animal and human feces into the polluted water as a test. I still think that this would begin to clean it up.

Fracking is spreading in a last-ditch effort to mine as much cheap energy as possible, leaving behind decimated areas, compromised drinking water supplies, and pollution seeping into underground waters and rivers. What sets hydraulic mining apart is the sheer volume of water used, and its permanent loss from the ecosystem. Depending on the site, hundreds of thousands of gallons of water are needed per well, meaning that billions of gallons of water are turned to poisonous wastewater and irreversibly removed from the water supply each year. "Safe" isolation of this wastewater is proving to be uncertain at best. The fracking industry is either unwilling or unable to deal with fracking's many risks: spills, well blowouts, unforeseen leaks of methane and other poisons that leach into groundwater, earthquakes triggered by injection wells, and the immense volume of wastewater fracking generates. Nor is there serious incentive, as fracking is exempt from the federal Resource Conservation Recovery Act (RCRA), which gives a framework to regulations for hazardous waste management.

One example of regulation: the government of Alberta requires that companies remediate and reclaim 100% of the land after the oil sands have been extracted. Reclamation means that land is returned to a self-sustaining ecosystem with local vegetation and wildlife. Will this happen? How long will it take to restore the land? What is permanently lost in the process of destruction and reclamation? Can we afford such losses?

The urgency of the extraction crisis cannot be understated or simplified. Regulations must not be written by the same extractive industries those regulations are intended to reign in. Every extractive industry must be carefully regulated, and these regulations must be international so that companies can't exploit countries that don't have regulations in place.

Consider that water extraction for bottling may prove to be the worst thing for life on earth. Nestlé,[37] Coca-Cola,[38] Pepsi,[39] and many more are privatizing water supplies, rapidly sucking pristine water from the earth, bottling it, and shipping it around the world. It follows that the privatization of water needs careful regulation, and public supplies need to be created and celebrated.

Dams

There are an estimated 84,000 dams in the U.S., impounding 600,000 miles of river or about 17% of rivers in the nation by length.[40] A large dam is defined by the dam industry as one higher than fifteen meters (taller than a four-story building). There are more than 57,000 large dams worldwide.

There are so many dams that the system is overwhelmed. Dam failure is a serious flood risk. Dam repairs and upkeep become more costly with age. Dams block upstream aquatic life movement and reduce downstream water quality by capturing sediment and cooler water—creating warmer, less sedimented water downstream, thus greatly affecting those ecosystems. Dam removal is a large project that can bring together many local and government bodies, potentially involving local citizens as well.[41]

Dams are now causing more harm than good. We know the optimal size of a dam for the purposes of generating electricity. More than that, we can generate electricity from other renewable sources. Dams decay and break, and have a limited life span. The average age of a dam in the United States is fifty years old. Nearly a third of our dams are considered hazardous.[42] We've removed over 1,300 of our 80,000 dams already, and need to continue this work.[43]

DESIGNS FOR COMPLEXITY AND RESILIENCE

Science Reveals

"If there is magic on this planet; it is contained in water."
—LOREN EISELEY, *The Immense Journey*, 1957

*"Complexity is the impossibility of
separating a system from its context."*
—ALBERT SVENT-GYORGY, 2017

I have read Albert Svent-Gyorgy's words over and over to digest the vast implications of his statement. The phrase "impossibility of separating" immediately challenges our minds, which have been rigorously taught that separating things in order to understand them is the correct approach.

This quote exposes the limits of a scientific methodology that insists on separating something from its context. The pursuit of knowledge through the classical scientific method excludes many questions and possibilities, thus only accounting for a small fraction of what happens in the natural world. By its very parameters, traditional science inevitably leads to single-purpose design.

The word *complex* is very different from the word *complicated*. The word *complicated* describes mechanical systems—like building a rocket or an airplane. *Complicated* systems are built from discrete objects that can be separated from their environment. A living system is *complex*. *Complex* systems are made of more parts than can be measured, at least so far, even with advanced computing.

Having unexplainable moments with water and noticing many energetic responses in my body, I was ever curious about H2O molecules and how they move, create, and impact life. Curiosity led me to explore the work of Masaru Emoto and others who are diving deep into the question of how water creates life. My investigations led me to a conference initiated by Dr. Gerald H. Pollack, in Sofia, Bulgaria, in 2016.

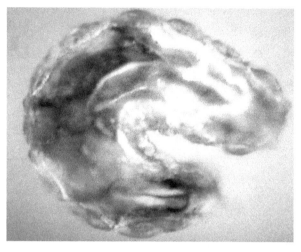

Mae-Wan Ho's photograph indicating a rainbow in
the embryo of a Drosophila larva (photo by Mae-Wan Ho)

At this conference, I had the privilege of meeting biophysicist Mae-Wan Ho, who began her journey in 1985 by asking how acupuncture works. She was the first to observe that the hydrogen molecule ran quickly through the body, creating a small electrical current. Later she observed that every embryo contains a complete rainbow. Her book, *The Rainbow and the Worm*, describes her journey to discover what life is and how it is created. The pictures of a tiny new life containing the complete rainbow were more than compelling—*how amazing*, I thought. In her final book, *The Meaning of Life and the Universe,* Mae-Wan Ho states clearly that water is the singular enabler of life. Water is the means, medium, and message. According to Mae-Wan Ho, "water is quantum coherent under ordinary conditions, according to a quantum electrodynamics field theory that may explain many of its most paradoxical properties including life itself." What does this mean? This means that water uniquely functions the same, wherever it is.

The leaders who evolved this perspective in physics were David Bohm and others who reformulated quantum theory based on universal wholeness. There are a number of notable physicists on this path, but the work of Italian theoretical physicist Emilio Del Giudice stands out. He discovered that water creates crystalline formations, and that there is a small electrical current in those formations that generates life. "Water is quantum coherent even under ambient conditions"—in other words, wherever it goes, water is always H_2O, although the molecules can take many millions of forms. Molecular structures change without changing chemical structures. This is clearly demonstrated in snowflakes; each snowflake is different, and yet every snowflake is water. We, too, are all different, and yet we are all the same. There is no way yet to measure the immense variations, connections, and possibilities water creates.

> *"There is the unity whereby one creature is united with the others and all parts of the world constitute one world."*
> —GIOVANNI PICO DELLA MIRANDOLA (1463–1494)

In two separate studies, both Mae-Wan Ho and Stanford University's William Tiller played music to water and noticed how the molecules responded, rearranging themselves constantly. This research was their biggest in-lab proof of the ability of water molecules to respond infinitely. Most of the research was focused on studying the power of water molecules by finding and examining a static replicable form of water. But then they tried to look at water on a deeper level. They tried to find out how water moved in response to influences. This led to the knowledge that life is a biodynamic process of creation—a process we know precious little about. Mae-Wan Ho created an experiment in which she watched water molecules change to the rhythm of jazz music.

Universal wholeness implies that within a field, many parts might appear to be acting independently even though they are acting synergistically. Scientists have sought to know the invisible, rather than discarding the unseeable and immeasurable as unimportant. Indigenous knowledge has long acknowledged that the immeasurable and invisible gives agency to the natural world—to mountains, waters, and stones.

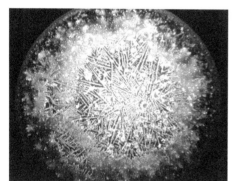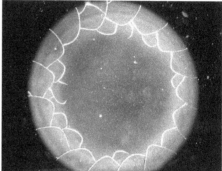

*Bernd Kroplin's water-drop photography (**permission pending**)*

The image above is a distillation of an incredible amount of pioneering research on water. Most significant is that water is collaborative and cooperative under any condition, which is the same as saying it is coherent under ambient conditions. Water is both sensitive and flexible. It responds to light and magnetic fields. Recent research has revealed some insights into how a drop of H_2o functions to create and respond to life. While there is some understanding about that drop, we are far from knowing all.

Starting with some facts, the human body is at least 75% water; our brains and hearts are 78%. The health of the ocean can be measured by examining just one drop. Water is an information carrier that changes the blood and tissues and reflects the very character of human consciousness. Currently, the possibility that water exhibits characteristics of consciousness is being explored. The nature of this consciousness is being debated. However, the debate is not about whether particles are embedded with consciousness, but about *which* particles and how to prove it. This suggests that it is the water-based functionality of the brain that facilitates humans' powerful information processor. A few brave souls propose not only that all life begins with water, but also that consciousness itself originates in water and directly depends on water quality. Every single cell of our body is around 70% water. We are singularly dependent on water and the same is true for all living creatures.

While controversy surrounds these issues, Dr. Jacques Benveniste, famous for his breakthroughs in the search for a cure for HIV, proved in 2014 that water has something tantamount to memory. He writes:

> *Water brings a pre-existing impulse to life. It creates the structure of DNA and proteins. Every seed and embryo begins in water, the carrier of the biological intelligence that is the determiner and means of change. Evidence shows that any substance that makes contact with water leaves a trace upon it. However, human emotions are the strongest influence. Water constitutes, migrates, and interpenetrates everything. All is connected by water. We can change our world, via water, by the conscious use of thought and feeling.*

After thirty-five years of listening to water, I have come to understand that all forms flow according to the principles of water. Our body is a flow system. All species are flow systems. Earth is a flow system. All these systems are interconnected, constantly communicating with each other. If we destroy one part, we affect all others. The massive species die-offs are impacting everyone. The large interventions in our rivers impact all life. Earth itself is a pulsing system and within it are the billions of pulses of life and living systems.

The earth is a giant container of sources of water. How humanity understands the quality of thoughts and feelings toward water affects in real terms the quality of what we drink. While traveling with Tibetans, I learned that they believe you can restore a well or a spring by circumambulating it 109 times while chanting a prayer. Love increases the frequency of imprints upon water. Thought is everything internally and acts externally.

Now, over twenty years after writing *Mistress Water* in 1990, I am reading Robin Kimmerer's book, *Braiding Sweetgrass*. Kimmerer describes the Ojibwemowin language. In this language, the living world has agency. For example, *bay* is a verb, not a noun: "The verb *wiikwegamaa*—to be a bay—releases the water from bondage and lets it live. 'To be a bay' holds the wonder that, for this moment, the living water has decided to shelter itself between these shores."

The English language seems inadequate to express the reality that nature has agency. If water's real role in creating life were ever-present in our minds, human perspective would make it impossible to reduce water to a material resource to be controlled, bought, and sold.

If water acts as a neurotransmitter between life forms, taking in information from the mental states of animals, plants, and all living forms, and carrying ripple effects outward, then we must begin to view all life in the universe as being one single macro-organism. Indigenous cultures have long known this to be true: that there is no "part" of nature, only a "whole." Indigenous cultures have a consciousness of the absolute interdependence of people and nature. This perspective confronts the exploitation and destruction of nature.

The living world is alive, communicating beyond human imagination, and needs humans to listen and take part. Nature is speaking clearly. She is saying, "I am one indivisible ecosystem; all living forms are interdependent." Water is our collective knowing, both consciously and unconsciously. What if this collective knowing were embedded and articulated in our culture? What if it were part of our teachings? Knowing this, would we continue to dam the places where the salmon run? How like salmon are we?

We did not come into this world. We came out of it, like buds out of branches and butterflies out of cocoons. We are a natural product of this Earth, and if we turn out to be intelligent beings, then it can only be because we are fruits of an intelligent Earth, which is nourished in turn by an intelligent system of energy."
—LYALL WATSON, *Gifts of Unknown Things*

Historically, humans have not been able to comprehend the trillions of connections that our waters facilitate every minute. The needed step is to honor and work with the strength of those connections and to learn how to live our lives according to water. What would this look like? Earth's future would be defined by how we structure our relationship to water. Humanity's future will depend on how water directs our decisions.

Water will not adapt to us, no matter how hard we try to force it. Embracing complexity is a big step. Although we are not yet able to decode the infinite capacity of water, we can begin to work with her to restore and revitalize.

"The day science begins to study nonphysical phenomena, it will make more progress in one decade than in all the previous centuries of its existence." —NIKOLA TESLA

Global Warming—Climate Change

Several hurricanes have now swept through many countries in a short time, destroying much in their paths. Sea levels are rising and most places are not prepared for these unprecedented events. We cannot predict and react to increases in the strength of hurricanes well enough to prevent the devastation on major

populations. Nature is innately powerful—she's powerful in creating, and in the process of creating, destroying to create again.

It is becoming increasingly clear that what happens on one side of the globe affects the other. One example of this interdependence is the coastal conditions of California, which depends on the Brazil-ian rainforest for moisture. The giant redwoods have been depleted. First, they were nearly all cut down, and more recently they suffered severe draughts because Amazonian deforestation deprives them of the rain they need.[44] With the significant loss of rainforest area, there is not enough evaporation from the rainforests of Brazil to give the coast of California the moisture it once received. The pulses and rhythms of the earth are being altered.

Forests

Trees are a good example. Humans depend on trees for our ability to live on earth. Trees are our fabulous ancestors who prepared the way for humans to be on earth. We are just beginning to understand the extraordinarily complex functions they serve. Like our waters, trees have been commodified.

Trees work together in groves, communicating and collaborating. We plant them in single rows in our cities along our streets—not the best way to have strong trees. Planting trees in two rows, and in small groves, would do so much more to increase their resiliency. Watersheds depend on trees as do billions of species.

Understanding trees and their multiple functions would make cities more liveable. 30% of the world's crops are dependent on cross-pollination by bees.[45] Bees are dependent on certain flowers that are free of pesticides.

TWO BOOKS ON TREES:
The Global Forest by Diana Beresford-Kroeger
The Man who Planted Trees by Jim Robbins

As human beings, we owe our existence to trees. We can live on earth only because there are trees. Trees are tall, walking beings that evolved well before humans, preparing the conditions in which humans could begin to thrive. They are negotiators of our atmosphere, holding the waters in the earth, returning water to the sky, cooling, absorbing, and transmitting. Trees live in communities: the parent trees care for the next generation and they communicate through the root systems to assist each other.[46] When one tree weakens, others come to help it. Forests work with water in profoundly connected systems. Trees filter pollutants from both air and water, provide homes for wildlife, offer outdoor classrooms to students of forestry and biology, slow soil erosion, and improve water flow. Trees delay water infiltration, prevent the rise of a salty water table, and save farmers' crops.

Trees living in a line

Old trees have powerful genomes. Every time we cut down the largest trees and reduce a forest to new growth, we are depleting the genome of the forest and degrading the living system. You rarely see big, wonderful old trees anymore. When I see one, I am in awe. I want to lie on a branch. Some cultures celebrate these trees, tying prayers on the branches and a big rope of prayers around the trunk. Large old trees are genetically the fittest; they are equivalent to the living waters that pour out of the earth, which contain dynamic properties. Trees have a genetic code that we do understand, but ignore. This code created gigantic trees, which protect the earth; I imagine them with great branches protecting us smaller beings.

Unfortunately, trees have been reduced to a price tag, and are being logged faster than they are replanted. We've lost more than half of our forest area to wars, agriculture, and industry.[47] Many of these forests have been clear-cut, so none of the old trees were left alive to pass on their gene pool. New trees may not have the genetic traits required to survive extreme conditions like global warming and its associated weather events.[48] The fight to save our forests is not hopeless, though: in March of 2020, advocates for the Tongass

Forest, which contains more than one-third of the world's temperate rainforest, scored a huge legal victory in a ruling striking down proposed timber sales.[49] Forests like the Tongass, especially old growth forests, store billions of tons of carbon and slow global warming. Programs like Plant-for-the-Planet and the Trillion Tree Campaign are working hard to plant tree cover. In the words of Diana Beresford-Kroger, "Forests hold a green passport into the future to stop climate change."

Reforestation can restore the balance among water, air, and land. Ethiopia is reforesting their country, and more countries are recognizing the problem of deforestation. India has set two records in a row, in 2016 and 2017, for most trees planted in twenty-four hours. Over a million volunteers planted nearly fifty million trees in 2016, and sixty-six million in 2017. Similarly, China is "[planting] seedlings over an area equal to Ireland" every year.[50] India is approaching the goal of reforestation set by the Paris Climate Agreement.[51]

Every species deserves to be thought about. All species have their role. Bees play a central role in connecting many ecosystems; 30% of the world's crops are dependent on cross-pollination by bees. In other words, most meals you eat depend on bees. But bees are dying at an alarming rate. According to the University of Maryland, in 2018 American beekeepers reported losing about 41% of their honeybee colonies, a 3% increase in the recorded loss during the same period in 2017. The decimation of bee populations is due to habitat destruction, the widespread use of harmful pesticides, and invasive mites interfering with colonies. On a grassroots level, we can each do something to help the bees. We must stop using harmful fertilizers in our gardens. We can make bees feel welcome in our own backyards by prioritizing native species, and even letting a few dandelions grow. Last, we can try to buy vegetables grown locally. Long-distance industrial agriculture is largely to blame for this crisis, so we should do what we can to stop supporting the industry.

Modern water infrastructure is a lot of concrete: dams, canals, reservoirs. But as the world warms and population grows, those old approaches won't be enough to stave off catastrophe, according to a hundred-page United Nations report released this week. Humanity will have to start embracing techniques that mimic natural processes. (Zoë Schlanger, *Quartz*, March 21, 2018)

Right now, in 2022, at least thirteen large cities with populations ranging from thirteen to twenty million people are experiencing a water crisis. The list is rapidly growing: Cape Town, San Paulo, Mexico City, Jakarta, Miami, London, Tokyo, Cairo, Jakarta, Istanbul, and Moscow. Somehow, people thought that economic growth would take care of it all, and that we would address water after we developed. How often did I hear from my Chinese collaborators: develop first, clean up later. Begging the Water Bureau and the planning bureau to work together, I lost every discussion to development and politics, regardless of the reality. Politics demanded an illusion of water. Here in New York City, what was once a saltwater estuary has been constricted into a polluted canal, and along it high-rise buildings continue to sprout up. With the seas rising, this would have been a perfect place for the rising waters to come and go. Over time, mayors have allowed most of the vacant lots in New York City to be bought and sold, rather than adjust the taxes to appropriately tax wealth. These lots could have become urban forests that absorb CO_2 and cool the air.

Regardless of size, our cities will need to approach water and water systems with projects that embrace the ideas of connectivity, complexity, and community: projects such as small compact wastewater systems in each subsection, urban farms, rainwater collection wherever possible, and recycling gray water in apartments and homes. We also need to carefully consider where we're growing our food. Farmland in dry areas requires withdrawal and transport from distant watersheds, so we should prioritize farming in places where water is abundant. In the Netherlands, greenhouse farming has rapidly expanded, which significantly reduces water and fertilizer/pesticide use, and also makes agriculture less climate-vulnerable. Animal waste can be collected and converted into useful products like fertilizers. There are other uses that require further research, but it must not be permitted to drain into bodies of water.

Every business around the world needs to be accountable for its impact on the environment. Today, technology can aid industrial water systems to be cleaner and to recycle. Graywater can satisfy most non-potable water demands.

Water passes through our homes to wipe away human waste—these systems are a luxury that many people do not have. Although home use is a small fraction of total water use—in 2010, domestic water withdrawals in the U.S. accounted for 1% of the total[52]—committing to living water starts in our homes, where we can take easy steps like switching to eco-friendly laundry detergents and cleaning supplies.

Many communities, including yours, are already seeing the effects of climate change, as well as single-purpose design's failure to address the problem. When the atmosphere gets warmer, water evaporates more quickly, and warm air retains more humidity. This means that storms get more intense, and the intense rains lead to faster runoff and flooding, giving the earth little time to absorb water and recharge ground waters before the rainwater runs off elsewhere. Dry areas are getting drier, droughts are longer and more severe, and areas that get a lot of rain are receiving even heavier precipitation.

There are many infrastructures that we can change, from recycling gray water to capturing rain to adapting farming to the use of storm drains. Drip irrigation uses much less water than sprinklers that spray it through the air. Fertilizers and pesticides are generally overused; luckily, organic farming is a growing industry. All bodies of water near agriculture need to be protected by streamside buffer zones and planted trees.

Designs for Complexity and Resilience

We all—especially engineers, planners, and designers—need to carefully consider how the innate dynamism of a system can be maintained or enhanced. Working with nature is different from dominating her. To work with her we need to watch what she is doing, how she responds. To work *with* implies reconnection and not further separation of her parts..

There are many levels of designing for complexity and resilience. The most fundamental concept is that water must be the foundation of planning and design. If water is the foundation of planning and design, then all housing developments, shopping malls, parking lots, road systems, and transportation hubs need to have a water plan that contributes to the sustainable future of your community.

This basic planning for water will help prevent flooding. And together with trees and plants, it will increase the biodynamism of the landscape, and mitigate the dirty runoff from cars. Wildlife populations will increase, and air quality will improve.

The following pages illustrate only a few green infrastructures according to their function in interacting with water. Many books address these solutions and there are likely people in your community who are familiar and can help you. These solutions are arranged from micro to macro, small to large. The numerous possibilities of things you can do in your home or your backyard can be found in the appendix. Each design is also listed as being part of one or more categories. Categories include *Storage, Conveyance, Infiltration,* and *Treatment.* When studying maps and water balance, you will find that you need to store, move, infiltrate, or treat your water. Different communities have various needs, and this list makes it easier to quickly identify which designs are needed in your community.

Hopefully you'll be taking part in a collective effort that could snowball into a big project.

A few larger projects are included in this book. A big project would include one or more macro solutions. These larger projects invite community members and community institutions to work together to retain, clean, and divert water to improve your water usage and balance. All aspects, ranging from parks and farms to roads and development plots, will be part of the larger plan.

The work of rainwater harvesting expert Brad Lancaster offers detailed drawings of ways to capture rainwater and reuse it. Throughout history, people have invented a great many solutions, and there are many more to be invented; you might invent one that is suitable for your situation.

Micro Solutions (Your Yard, Your Land)

See appendix: These solutions are small-scale projects that anyone can implement in the home or in community spaces.

Macro Solutions

Catch-basin treatment systems: These are modified catch basins that clean water and grit, and remove oils and greases from the water. *(Storage, Treatment)*

Parking lot storage: Parking lots, plazas, and other hard surface areas can be designed with thin pipes and higher curbs to temporarily store water during storms. *(Storage)*

Pipe Storage: Pipes can be designed to perform functions other than rapidly conveying water. They can be over-sized so that they can store water underground. They can be small to restrict flow so that downstream systems aren't overwhelmed by runoff. *(Storage)*

Constructed wetland: Wetlands serve innumerable functions. For water storage, a clay-bottom soil-constructed wetland is particularly effective. Another advantage of constructed wetlands is that they have lots of gravel and root systems that hold and slow down water to aid infiltration. Yet another advantage of wetlands is that their diverse ecosystems can clean water with microorganisms similar to those used in municipal wastewater treatment facilities. Gravel, root systems, and bacteria aerate, filter, aerate, and clean organic waste. *(Storage, Infiltration, Treatment)*

Constructed wetlands from the Living Water Garden

Increasing Shoreline Capacity: Plants like mangroves prevent shoreline erosion, capture carbon, provide habitat for countless species, and weaken storm surges that threaten coastal communities. Mangroves, which thrive in the space between land and sea, support rich biodiversity and offer crucial sheltering habitat for sea life that feeds hundreds of millions of people.[53] Mangroves have been devastated by human activities. The Sri Lankan Mangrove Conservation Project is working to bring the reforestation movement to this unique environment between land and sea.[54]

Natural Filtration: Nature is always working. She cleans water as it moves through different ecosystems, especially wetlands.

Many water cleaning systems are designed to clean water naturally, in powerful and interesting ways. These systems clean water using plants, microbes, sunshine, or complex layers of rock, sand, and gravel. As water travels through certain places, it picks up particles, primarily minerals—some beneficial and some not. The accumulation of these minerals is why some water is hard and some is soft. I once visited a polluted reservoir north of Beijing. But to my surprise, when we walked below the dam, we could see clean waters and deduced that there must be an area underneath with a lot of sand that was cleaning the water. After oil spills, microbes clean up the oil.[55] Oil has been in our environment and oceans for a long time and nature evolves her ways to clean it up. However, oil spills usually overwhelm the environment, killing much; the fact that nature can clean this up over time is not an excuse to ignore spills.

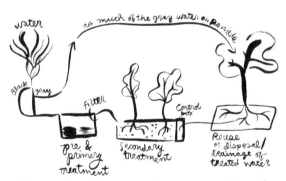

How plants filter water

Steps toward Complexity: Portland

Having initiated the Living Water Garden's iconic model of integrated design, it was clear to me that entire watersheds needed to be reworked according to the principles of the Living Water Garden. Scaling up would be the next step. Each community could begin to implement connectivity. Awakening people to water is the first step. Every invitation to do something in a community has been an opportunity for me to learn not only about their water but also about the numerous challenges and to brainstorm possible solutions. Groups organized around these projects.

A friend, Ann Mavor, asked me to visit Portland, where she introduced me to city planners who were exploring options for combined sewer overflow (CSO) issues. Combined sewer overflow means that stormwater and sewer water are diverted into the same pipes, so that when there is a lot of rain and the pipes overflow, the sewer overflows into the streets, parks, etc. Portland was making a decision between treating sewage overflow by using natural processes, or by means of an expensive pump and pipe project. Under the nonnatural plan, pipes would collect the overflow and pump it up a mountain to a treatment plant thirty miles away. But Portland's hilly ravine topography is ideal for stormwater capture, which would avoid the expensive "Big Pipe" option.

We held a workshop for activists, artists, environmentalists, educators, and landscape designers. One project emerged from this workshop: the eighth grade of the da Vinci Arts Middle School decided that converting an old tennis court into a stormwater capture park would be a great class project. This site became the host of a spring event promoting eco-innovations, environmental information, and organic farming. The project inspired many more like it, and the city adopted a new system in which many schools captured rainwater. Landscape design companies and city entities received funding for more rainwater capture and stormwater bioswales, which would prevent sewage overflow from reaching the river.

Da Vinci Water Garden

The "Big Pipe Project" was chosen and was partially completed in 2011. This helped to make the Willamette River clean enough for swimming. Within this system, many micro-solutions were implemented as well, because it was nearly impossible to remake the entire infrastructure. The Big Pipe Project is a single-purpose solution which is, in the short term, effective. But in the long run, these types of designs are inflexible: pipes and pumps decay. In contrast, living systems reuse and regenerate.

Complexity in Action: Restoration in Tehuacán

I had the privilege to meet Gisela Herrerías through the Global Network of Water Museums. Her organization, Agua para Siempre, has worked with Indigenous farmers to revitalize the land and grow crops suitable for the climate.

Herrerías and her partner Raúl Hernández Garciadiego realized that poverty in the Tehuacán Valley among the Popoloca community was less a result of the lack of money and had more to do with the lack of water. The local geology made drilling wells cost-prohibitive, so helping this community wasn't that simple. Herrerías and

Garciadiego took special care to avoid coming into a community and imposing their own visions and needs, and instead practiced radical listening. The two "used the method they learned in workshops led by José Luis Brito, who advocated a form of participative observation that required participant-observers to write notes in the exact words of the people with whom they interacted in an effort to exclude their own impressions."[56]

Planting amaranth

During this radical listening, someone mentioned a drought-resistant grain that had been grown in the Tehuacán Valley centuries ago: amaranth. The duo acquired some seeds and planted a field to test out the crop's resilience. To their surprise, when they returned to check on the crop a couple months later, the field was completely cleared, with not a trace of the amaranth left behind. As it turns out, people from the nearest village harvested and ate the amaranth, without needing to be told that the crop was edible. The easy return of amaranth to the Tehuacán Valley is an example of *biocultural memory* being activated.[57] This project was a success because it embraced Indigenous knowledge as a foundation and responded to Indigenous people's embrace of that knowledge.

Complexity in Action: Waste Enterprises

One of the most interesting—and implementable—projects I know is Ashley Murray Muspratt's Waste Enterprises. This Ghana-based start-up "turns raw human waste, or fecal sludge, into bio-fuel pellets, a commodity that sells for two hundred dollars a ton in some parts of Europe."[58] Ashley's company treats human waste as the only truly unlimited resource. Factories that manufacture industrial goods like cement burn cheap fossil fuels for energy. Meanwhile, rapid urbanization has led to a widespread sanitation crisis around the world. Waste Enterprises addresses these two problems with a single solution. Commodifying human waste instead of letting it seep into the natural environment means cleaner cities *and* less greenhouse gas from the factories that make the switch. One Fecal Fuel Facility treats the waste of 350,000 people. When this fuel is burned at factories, it offsets carbon emissions. Last, on a human level, this project generates more than two million dollars in annual revenue, and provides jobs.[59]

This project is a perfect example of the difference between *complex* and *complicated*. Although Waste Enterprises presents a simple solution, it engages with complexity because it closes a wasteful loophole in human activity. It makes both sanitation and manufacturing less *complicated* because it turns two wasteful pieces of infrastructure into one combined process. Last, Waste Enterprises mimics nature. In nature, animal waste is integrated into the ecosystem, providing food for plant life and even spreading seeds. This waste repurposing project makes human society function more like the natural world.

Complexity in Action: Loess Plateau

Humans have lived on the Loess Plateau—the birthplace of Chinese civilization—for more than 1.5 million years. Ever since the growth of agriculture around 10,000 years ago, the Loess Plateau's famously powdery soil has been slowly—then quickly—eroding away. It's currently one of the most eroded places on earth. One of the most devastating consequences of this erosion has been increased flooding, caused by riverbeds being filled in with sediment. The Yellow River even became known as "China's Sorrow" as a result of its destructive floods.[60]

Chinese planners from the Ministry of Water Resources and international planners from the World Bank worked together with experts in hydrology, soil dynamics, forestry, agriculture, and economics, to design a plan to restore the plateau. Farmers and herders agreed to give up their traditional ways of living to restore the land if they would, in return, receive an income and have the rights to use the land again once the project was finished.

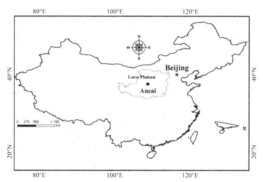

Location of the Loess Plateau

Loess Plateau before and after restoration[61]

The most significant thing to me was how much of the project was developed by and rooted in local knowledge. The local farmers proposed that they would stop grazing their animals and stop subsistence farming, and in turn they would do the terracing that would hold the waters up and create farmland. They would do all the work, and they asked for a salary and the right to own the land. In response, the project included a social component that clearly established land tenure, guaranteeing farmers the rights to their new erosion-resistant terraced fields.

The project also clearly defined ecological land, and economic land, and respected the impact each has on the other. Lands newly established as ecological were given a head start with massive reforestation and grasslands restoration. When nature is left to its own devices, it will self-regenerate, but this effort shows the power in actively helping nature restore itself.

The project was a success, as the above photograph shows. This restoration was extensively documented by filmmaker and ecologist John D. Liu. There is no limit to what is possible when we choose to restore a degraded system.

The success of the Loess Plateau restoration has inspired a Dutch holistic engineering firm called the Weather Makers to "regreen" the Sinai Peninsula. The Weather Makers' ambitious proposal engages directly with water's complexity to restore this arid region to its earlier, greener state: "Regreening the Sinai is to some extent a question of restarting that 'water begets water' feedback loop…restored wetlands would encourage more birds, which would add fertility and new plant species."[62] This project makes it clear that success stories in fighting climate chaos are contagious.

Complexity in Action: Elwha River Restoration

The large Elwha Dam was completed in 1913 in Washington, impounding the Elwha River to create a power station with a 14.8 megawatt capacity. In 1992, the Elwha dam project was handed over to the federal government for demolition, which was finally completed in 2012.

The Elwha River Dam was the largest dam removed in American history. The main intention was to restore the optimal breeding conditions for salmon, but this kind of major restoration always benefits more than one species. Damming the Elwha River had reduced sediment flow to the coast, which caused rapid erosion of the shoreline of the Elwha River delta. The Elwha River Restoration Project has resulted in over a meter of restored sedimentation in the estuary and over 400 meters of expansion of the river mouth delta. The Elwha River will likely be able to restore itself to its pre-dam state in the near future.[63]

Elwha River Dam removal in progress (source: Paul Cooper)

I find these projects inspiring and hopeful; they prove that real restoration can be done with thorough planning and holistic study. These are just a few of the efforts that have been made, and there are dozens of models to draw ideas from. These often start with just one person, and end up changing things in a big way. (See the appendix for more examples of ambitious projects like these.)

"Nature is not a place to visit. It is home."
—Gary Snyder

Recently, a colleague asked me how I stay hopeful. I replied that defeat is not an option. More to the point: what would defeat look like? And that, I do not like to imagine.

Complexity in Action: Newport Spring (by Ron Henderson)

The site of the Newport Spring, around which the original colonial settlers of Newport, Rhode Island settled, is returning to use as public space for the first time in 350 years. Newport was established on Aquidneck Island in 1639 by William Brenton and Company.[64]

The site of the spring appears on the redrawn version of Ezra Stiles' first map of Newport, one of only a few landmarks, including the harbor, that appear on this early map. The principles of religious freedom, for which Newport was the catalyst, led to the construction around the spring of Touro Synagogue, the first Jewish synagogue in the United States. Other religious structures founded in the immediate vicinity include the second Baptist Church in America, the Quaker Meetinghouse, and Trinity Episcopal Church. Clearly, Newport Spring was also a font of religious freedom.

It was soon discovered that fresh groundwater was readily available despite Newport being situated on an island surrounded by the saline waters of the Atlantic Ocean and Narragansett Bay. The spring, then, became a watering hole for horses and livestock around which grew blacksmiths, coopers, and other trades that catered to horses. In the early twentieth century, one of Rhode Island's first gasoline service stations opened on the site. The transition from serving horses to serving horseless carriages is not unexpected. For over a century, the site, at the corner of Spring Street and Touro Street, was a service station—most recently Coffey's Citgo.

In 2015, Neil Coffey retired, and a group of citizens with support from Rhode Island-based foundations purchased the property with the intent to return the spring to public use. That process is now underway. The most recent milestone was the remediation of contaminated soil. During this process, excavation discovered a pre-twentieth century half-cylinder well in which fifteen feet of water still springs forth. The design of the new public space, by Ron Henderson and Tanya Kelley of L&A Landscape Architecture, is awaiting archaeological and hydrological investigations, but will seek to amplify the potent natural history of this island freshwater site and the profound events of religious freedom that similarly sprung from the adjacent institutions. The Historic Newport Spring will become a public commons that celebrates the original spring around which the town was founded.

≈

In conclusion, we as a world body can choose that every human being has the right to water. In other words, no one should be able to destroy the water source of a community. Extractive industries pose an existential threat to our waters. Land that extraction destroys is called sacrificed land. We cannot sacrifice land. Extraction must be closely monitored to ensure that it never harms a community or its waters. Fracking needs to be banned. According to the NRDC, fracking causes $13–29 billion worth of health damages annually, with symptoms including "severe headaches, asthma symptoms, childhood leukemia, cardiac problems, and birth defects" along with cancers.[65] Writing this book has helped me realize that in an ideal world, every living form would have all the water it needs.

After writing this book, I realized more than ever that, ideally and in the best of all possible worlds, no life form would be without water. The main destruction of our waters comes from extraction. The flow of rivers should be maintained to maintain the right balance.

Conclusion: The Power of Us

"Life appears to be quantum electro-dynamical through and through, and water is at the heart of it all."
—Mae-Wan Ho, *Life is Water Electric*

"Nothing is too wonderful to be true if it is consistent with the laws of nature." —Michael Faraday

Our journey with water is just beginning. Sixty years ago, Loren Eiseley wrote, *If there is magic on this planet, it is contained in water.* Now we know the magic is in the molecular power of water to endlessly create and restore over and over again. Although we still have much to discover, it is clear that water molecules are far more powerful than we currently understand. Biochemist Gilbert Ling describes life as "water electric."

It is consistent with the laws of nature that we human beings collaborate. The universe is a vast, collaborative, living network, and biophysicists are beginning to decode it. We are far from understanding how it works. A quantum electrodynamic universe is the best model we have moving forward in these times. This model is a distinct contradiction to the notion of a dog-eat-dog world. Who is left after predators gobble up everyone else?

Major solutions to climate change and pollution can be found within water. Biochemistry is rapidly approaching this reality. It is just possible and even likely that consciousness is inseparable from water. This consciousness is everywhere. It is complexity at work.

Even if you have your doubts about whether these incredible drops are embedded with consciousness, start your own inquiry. Nature is speaking clearly. She is saying, *I am one indivisible ecosystem; all living forms are interdependent, connected by water.* Begin, and you will connect.

The Balkans contain some of the last free-flowing rivers in Europe. But in 2017, word spread that Bosnia and Herzegovina's Kruščica River was going to be dammed without the consent of the community. A grassroots coalition led by women, called the Brave Women of Kruščica, have disrupted the project. Over 200 people joined together to occupy a bridge, blocking machinery from crossing over. The community organized shifts to maintain the blockade twenty-four hours a day, seven days a week, for 500 consecutive days. The Brave Women of Kruščica stalled construction long enough to open a legal case against the project, and are hopeful about the outcome.[66]

Around the world there are grassroots movements to stop pipelines, dams, mines, and bottling. These efforts are rarely given the press they deserve.

The work of water is far greater than we have been able to measure. She is the mistress of all life. Water molecules are powerful, full of more information than we know. When a small stream is restored, the surrounding waters are activated, begging to join. Similarly, when people are healthy, they can think clearly. Others will listen to them and desire to be like them.

It is time to ignite international conversations about how to secure living water systems for all life on earth. These conversations must be rooted in a perspective that water has rights, exactly the same rights as every living form. These conversations cannot continue to be defined and controlled by private ownership, bottling companies, or governments that would like to build more dams and more water transfers. The world needs a deliberative body to determine ecological impacts on its water, and to ensure that disruptive projects minimize their impact on ecosystems.

As I complete this book, the coronavirus is circulating the globe. We are experiencing a pause and a pivot. We are experiencing shock, grief, and hope. We are observing the benefits of a pause in the cruise ship industry, a 17% decrease in CO_2 emissions, air quality improvements, and decreased consumerism. The earth is taking a deep breath. The dolphins can breathe, the whales are calmer in their waters. I can feel the increased pulse of life around me.

Reach beyond words and imagine living water—the lifeblood of all systems—sustaining and being sustained by those systems. Imagine a network of living waters constantly growing, revitalizing vast areas, and sustaining ecosystems to supply billions of people and all life with clean water. Let's assume for one minute that pulses are connected in some undetectable way. When we restore one pulse in a water system—such as through dam removal, daylighting, or the removal of pollutants—this affects life far beyond that single water system or community.

Human beings are innately connected to the creative power of water. We are privileged to live in a complex natural world that is much larger and more interdependent within her systems than we have understood. We've invented ways to explore Mars and communicate instantly around the world. But we have not created another Earth. None of our creations are as great or as complex as the earth itself. Let's put to work our resources, our passion, our love of life, our desire to create, to rejoin a living system.

We need unwavering commitment to protect and restore life-sustaining water. It will take all of us cooperating and collaborating—artists, scientists, engineers, planners, government officials, teachers, and people from all walks of life—to accomplish this life-saving task. Around the world, we can join with the flow of waters and revitalize Earth's veins.

The singular reality is that we are all connected—to each other, and to our waters. As this book was streaming toward publication, I learned about a global citizen-led movement to implement a

World Water Law. The proposal for a World Water Law invites all of humanity to unite around the radical healing of the planetary waters and water cycle. This foundational law will work to ensure that all humans and animals have guaranteed access to natural, uncontaminated water. It will hold each and every individual, organization, business, sector, and government fully accountable for their impact on water. Ultimately, the World Water Law will activate an exponential whole-system healing response that addresses many of the root causes of our escalating global challenges.

APPENDIX

DESIGNS FOR COMPLEXITY AND RESILIENCE

Micro Solutions

Tree wells, garden irrigation, green wall: Easily constructed water diversions for home landscapes. A tree well is a simple underground system built around the base of a tree with stones that delay water near the tree roots to be filtered naturally. You can build downslopes to direct water toward your garden. A green wall augments dull impervious architecture with vertically growing plants that use and filter water as it flows down the wall. *(Storage)*

Rain barrel: Widely available containers for holding water (it can even be a trash can) usually connected to the end of a downspout. You can use this water for anything at home, and can even treat it and drink it. *(Storage)*

Roof Storage: Collected roof water can be diverted to various storage containers. Those open and above ground will encourage evaporation. *(Storage)*

Pond, stormwater pond: Open-air ponds storing runoff from roofs and parking lots. Stormwater ponds are built specifically for controlling flooding by collecting and storing stormwater. *(Storage)*

Roof chains: Chains or chain-like designs that hang from gutters. As opposed to downspouts, chains slow down and aerate the water as it falls. *(Conveyance)*

Flowforms: Sculptural designs that convey water in a vortex form to slow, aerate, and regenerate water. *(Conveyance, Treatment)*

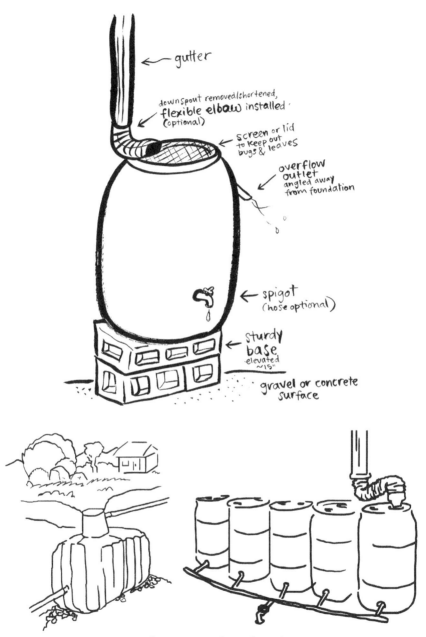

← gutter

downspout removed/shortened,
flexible elbow installed
(optional)

screen or lid
to keep out
bugs & leaves

overflow
outlet
angled away
from foundation

← spigot
(hose optional)

← sturdy
base
elevated
~15"

gravel or concrete
surface

Three types of rain barrels

Bioswales: A landscaped contour that allows water to spread out on a deliberately vegetated surface. This conveys the water slowly, providing interaction with plants to treat the water as it flows. The earth has many natural filtering systems that get disturbed by single-purpose design. A good example is the edge of roads. When we allow runoff to return to the earth, there are many positive effects. We can increase those effects by creating sand and gravel filtering systems along the sides of roads. *(Conveyance)*

Bioswale

Bioswale

French drains: Trenches filled with gravel and lined with plastic, clay tiles, or another non-porous material. They can be used instead of pipes and as footing drains around your house to direct water away from the foundation. Gravel acts as a filter for large debris and as a surface for healthy microbes to flourish and pre-treat water. *(Conveyance, Infiltration, Treatment)*

Plants and trees: Vegetation not only slows down water to allow it to infiltrate, but also improve soil structure, creating channels with its roots that quickly convey water underground. *(Infiltration)*

Roof materials: Capturing and reusing our rainwater and returning it to the land is one of the most important things we can do to address water scarcity and water excess. Rainwater capture starts with the roof. To repurpose rainwater into drinking water, you will need to use contaminant-free roofing materials and include a filtration system. As far as roofing materials go, tin is one of the best materials to use for a rainwater harvesting project because it carries no risk of contaminants. Wood is generally a poor material for this purpose, as it leaches contaminants into your water. For this reason, it's important to trim tree branches from overhanging the roof, since branches can drop their own contaminants. Filtration isn't necessarily best when capturing water for watering a garden, washing cars and homes, or other outdoor purposes. These uses are also compatible with lower-grade roofing materials like shingles, ceramic, and cement. Another factor to consider is water loss through evaporation: darker materials heat up more in the sunlight, leading to higher rates of evaporation when rainwater hits the roof. Consider painting darker metals with an approved, non-contaminating lighter coating, like NSF-61.[67]

Rain gardens: Deliberately constructed low areas to hold water temporarily, so it can seep into the ground before being swept out onto streets and into storm drains. *(Infiltration)*

Low-flow showerheads, toilets, and graywater appliances: Low flow showers and appliances that recycle gray water can reduce home water use by nearly a third, lessening the load on wastewater treatment. *(Treatment)*

Composting toilets: Toilets that allow us to reduce human waste in sewage, and also provide fertilizer for your own garden or your communities. Popular for boats to meet overboard discharge requirements. *(Treatment)*

Plants are a water technology unto themselves.

Drinking water fountains: Let's make plastic bottles obsolete. Drinking fountains were once a sacred part of urban life. Today, they're in crisis, mostly because of bottled water and the bottling industry's misinformation campaigns. "Water fountains have been disappearing from public spaces throughout the country over the last few decades," says Nancy Stoner, an EPA administrator.[68] The disappearance of water fountains has been disastrous for public health. A researcher with the Centers for Disease Control who spoke with the *Washington Post* found that "the less young people trust water fountains, the more sugary beverages they drink."[69] This puts young people at increased risk of developing obesity-related illnesses such as

Type-2 diabetes. Bottled water is also terrible for the environment. The amount of oil required per year to produce America's bottles would be enough to power 100,000 cars for a year. Last, bottled water is infinitely more expensive than water from a water fountain. In other words, bottled water is bad for the environment, bad for our wallets, and bad for us.

Swimming pools: Pools and other water features can be fed with rainwater to mitigate heavy stormwater loads and supplement fire suppression and drinking water supply. *(Storage)*

Filters: The biosand filter comprises a container—plastic or concrete—and is about the size of an office water cooler. It has an inset plastic pipe and is filled with layers of sand and gravel. Dirty water is poured into the top of the biosand filter, where a diffuser plate evenly distributes the water over the sand bed layer. Sand and gravel are natural filters. The roots of plants also actively work to collect pollution. When roots are wrapped around small stones or in the earth, they draw contaminants up and into the leaves.

Macro Solutions

Lakes: The most well-known system of water storage is the water supply lake, frequently created by damming to control its level. *(Storage)*

Groundwater: Water sitting among rock and soil underground can act as very effective storage—the sun and plants cannot easily drain groundwater. Many communities are now directly piping their surface runoff to their groundwater. *(Storage)*

Check dams: Any form of small dam placed on slopes in swales and at the edges of parking lots, to slow down the flow of water. *(Conveyance)*

Porous pipes: Pipes that are perforated with holes or made from porous materials so that they allow some water to sink into the earth.

Multiple outfalls: Single pipes that release water do so at a high speed which can scour river and stream bottoms. Spreading the water flow into many different outfalls can solve this problem. *(Conveyance, Infiltration)*

Porous pavements: Materials that allow water to permeate, rather than completely covering the surface. These include concrete blocks with grid shapes, gravel, and special asphalts. *(Conveyance)*

Street cleaning and garbage collection: A major source of contamination is runoff from dirty human surfaces—the cleaner we keep them, the cleaner runoff will be; especially clearing leaves, which can overwhelm pipes and streams. *(Treatment)*

First flush treatment: Rainfall on dirty, urban, impervious surfaces is dirtiest in the first inch or two of rainfall (about 5 minutes). You can treat this water in wetlands or other green infrastructures, by using systems on timers that divert that water. You can achieve a timing system with pipes at different levels. *(Treatment)*

Open-bottom culverts: A culvert brings a stream underground to pass under a road or railroad. Opening the bottom to the earth slows down the water allowing fish passage, infiltration, and contact with rocks and plants. Cities have very set ways to do things. Everything is sized, and therefore inflexible. Each repair is a predetermined set of solutions. This cannot respond to climate change. *(Conveyance, Infiltration)*

Riverbank stabilization: High volumes of runoff can scour the bottoms of streams and rivers. Adding plant material and rock and widening the bank can all increase resilience by slowing down runoff. *(Conveyance, Infiltration)*

Gravels, infiltration ditches: Unlike French drains which convey water away, these are large underground gravel systems where runoff can be directed to slowly sink into the ground. *(Infiltration)*

Ecological treatment/living machines: These are treatment systems for residential sewage that can be developed on a neighborhood scale to reduce organic waste in your water. They can be developed into community greenhouses and provide great educational opportunities. *(Treatment)*

Biological treatment: Standard wastewater treatment that uses monocultures of microorganisms to treat wastewater on a large scale. *(Treatment)*

≈

KEEPERS OF THE WATERS CHENGDU

Participating Artists & Facilitators

*It took many collaborators to implement
this project; this is a partial list:*

Betsy Damon, Director	United States
Zhu Xiaofeng, Director	China
Wang Peng	Beijing
Yin Xiuzhen	Beijing
Zhang Xuehua	Chengdu
Lin Shao Han, Director of Water Quality	Chengdu
Dai Guangyu	Chengdu
Zhong Bo	Chengdu
He Qichao	Chengdu
Liu Changing	Chengdu
Zeng Xun	Chengdu
Yang Lijun	Chengdu
Xu Hongbin	Chengdu
Yang Lijun	Chengdu
Cai Jian	Chengdu
Yang Qi	Chengdu
Zhu Cheng	Chengdu
Yin Xiaofeng	Chengdu
Yu Lieqing	Shanghai
Ang Sang	Tibet
Ciren Lanmu	Tibet
Jon Otto	United States
Jill Jacoby, scientist	United States
Ann Pilli, biologist	United States
Kristin Caskey, assistant	United States
Chris Baeumler	United States
Beth Grossman	United States
Laurie Perlow, photographer	United States

A Memory of Clean Water

Participating Artists & Collaborators
It takes a village to create a piece like this.

Project Director	Robyn Stein
Master papermakers	Helmut Becker, Coco Gordon, Ray Tomasso, Lucy Wallingford
Artists	Regina Corritore, Denise Amses
Filming and editing	Victor Masayesva
Video assistant	Patricia Walsh
Photography	Patricia Switzer
Special thanks to:	Joe Kingsley, Elisa Love, Joy Gordon, Christina Biaggi, Scott Portman, Duane Griffin, George Shultz

Recommended Organizations

The Center for Maximum Potential Building Systems	cmpbs.org
Codes for a Healthy Earth	codes.earth
Ecoart Network	ecoartnetwork.org
Ecoart Space	ecoartspace.org
Global Network of Water Museums	watermuseums.net
Guardians Worldwide	guardiansworldwide.org
Keepers of the Waters	keepersofthewaters.org
Think about Water	thinkaboutwater.com
Together in Creation	togetherincreation.org
UNITY EARTH	unity.earth
Walking Water	walking-water.org
Women Eco Artists Dialogue	weadartists.org
World Water Community	worldwatercommunity.com

Recommended Reading

Barry, Joyce. "Mountaineers Are always Free? An Examination of Mountaintop Removal Mining in West Virginia," *Women's Studies Quarterly,* summer 2001.

Brown, Lester R. *Eco-Economy: Building an Economy for the Earth.* New York: Routledge, 2001.

Bullard, Robert D. *Confronting Environmental Racism: Voices from the Grassroots.* Boston: South End Press, 1999.

———. *Dumping in Dixie: Race, Class, and Environmental Quality* (3rd ed.). Routledge, 2000.

Coats, Callum *Living Energies: An Exposition of Concepts Related to the Theories of Viktor Schauberger.* UK: Gateway, 1996.

Colborn, Theo, Dianne Dimanoski, and John Peterson Myers. *Our Stolen Future: Are We Threatening Our Fertility, Intelligence and Survival? A Scientific Detective Story.* New York: Plume, 1996.

Consigli MD, Dr. Paolo. *Water, Pure and Simple: The Infinite Wisdom of an Extraordinary Molecule.* UK: Watkins, 2008.

Dreiseitl, Herbert, Dieter Grau, Karl Ludwig. *Waterscapes: Planning, Building and Designing with Water.* Boston: Birkhäuser, 2001.

Egan, Dave, Evan E. Hjerpe, Jesse Abrams (eds.). *The Human Dimensions of Ecological Restoration: Integrating Science, Nature, and Culture.* Washington, DC: Island, 2011.

Geffen, Amara, Ann Rosenthal, Chris Fremantle and Aviva Rahmani. *Ecoart in Action: Activities, Case Studies, and Provocations for Classrooms and Communities.* New York: New Village Press, 2022.

Goodall, Jane. *Harvest for Hope : A Guide to Mindful Eating.* New York: Warner, 2005.

Harrison, Helen Mayer and Newton Harrison. *The Time of the Force Majeure: After 45 Years Counterforce is on the Horizon.* Munich: Prestel, 2016.

Hawken, Paul. *Regeneration: Ending the Climate Crisis in One Generation.* Penguin, 2021.

Kimmerer, Robin. *Braiding Sweetgrass: Indigenous Wisdom, Scientific Knowledge and the Teachings of Plants.* New York: Penguin, 2020.

LaDuke, Winona. *All Our Relations: Native Struggles for Land and Life.* Cambridge, MA: South End Press, 1999.

Lancaster, Brad. *Rainwater Harvesting for Drylands and Beyond.* Tucson: Rainsource Press, 2008.

Lippard, Lucy R. *Undermining: A Wild Ride Through Land Use, Politics, and Art in the Changing West.* The New Press, 2014.

McKibben, Bill; *Deep Economy: The Wealth Of Communities and the Durable Future*. New York: Times Books, 2007.

Pollan, Michael; *The Botany of Desire: The Plant's-Eye View of the World*. New York: Random House, 2001.

Schwenk, Theodor. *Sensitive Chaos: The Creation of Flowing Forms in Water and Air*. Forest Row, UK: Rudolf Steiner Press, 2008.

Schwenk, Theodor, and Wolfram Schwenk: *Water: the Element of Life*. Hudson NY: Anthroposophic Press, 1990.

Schwenk, Wolfram (ed.). *The Hidden Qualities of Water*. Edinburgh: Floris Books, 2007.

———. *Water as an Open System*. H. Dreiseitl et al. (eds.). Basel and Boston: Birkhäuser, 2001.

———. *The Mobility of Water as an Aspect of Quality and its Visualization by Means of the Drop Picture Method*. Kozisek F. (ed.). Prague: Living Water, 1995.

Shiva, Vandana: *Water Wars*. Cambridge, MA: South End Press, 2002.

Smith, Mick. *An Ethics of Place: Radical Ecology, Postmodernity and Social Theory*. Albany, NY: SUNY, 2001.

Spaid, Sue. "Tying Climate Justice to Hydrological Justice." *Rivista di Estetica*, Issue 75, 2020.

Wenk, Bill. *Working Water: Design Beyond the Garden Wall*. ORO Editions, 2021.

———. *Working Water: Reinventing the Storm Drain*. ORO Editions, 2022.

ENDNOTES

1   Universal Declaration of Human Rights (n.d.). Retrieved Dec. 28, 2020, from https://www.un.org/en/universal-declaration-human-rights/index.html.

2   "The human rights to safe drinking water and sanitation" (PDF). Retrieved Nov. 27, 2020.

3   O'Donnell, Erin, and Julia Talbot-Jones. "Three Rivers Are Now Legally People – but That's Just the Start of Looking after Them." The Conversation, Oct. 21, 2019, theconversation.com/three-rivers-are-now-legally-people-but-thats-just-the-start-of-looking-after-them.

4   Steen B. "Body water in the elderly—a review." J Nutr Health Aging. 1997;1(3):142-5. PMID: 10995081.

5   Young, Hayley A, and David Benton. "Heart-Rate Variability: a Biomarker to Study the Influence of Nutrition on Physiological and Psychological Health?" Behavioural Pharmacology, Lippincott Williams and Wilkins, Apr. 2018, www.ncbi.nlm.nih.gov/pmc/articles/PMC5882295.

6   Emoto, Masaru, and Tokujiro Kawasaki. "The Message from Water: The Message from Water Is Telling Us to Take a Look at Ourselves." HADO Kyoikusha, 2000.

7   Langeland, K.A., and Lyn A. Gettys. "Safe Use of Glyphosate-Containing Products in Aquatic and Upland Natural Areas." *IFAS Extension*, https://edis.ifas.ufl.edu/pdffiles/AG/AG24800.pdf.

8   "Monsanto Guilty in 'False Ad' Row." *BBC News*, BBC, Oct. 15, 2009, news.bbc.co.uk/2/hi/europe/8308903.stm.

9   Monsanto Papers: Secret Documents (n.d.). Retrieved Dec. 28, 2020, from https://www.baumhedlundlaw.com/toxic-tort-law/monsanto-roundup-lawsuit/monsanto-secret-documents/.

10   Beth Grossman. "Dreams for a Pure River." http://www.bethgrossman.com/gallery/publicart/pureriver/.

11   See http://www.nytimes.com/gwire/2009/07/09/09greenwire-fewer-regulations-for-bottled-water-than-tap-g-33331.html

12   See https://www.nrdc.org/stories/truth-about-tap.

13   Pierre-Louis, K. (2015). "We don't trust drinking fountains anymore, and that's bad for our health." Retrieved Oct. 30, 2020, from https://www.washingtonpost.com/opinions/we-dont-trust-drinking-fountains-anymore-and-thats-bad-for-our-health/2015/07/02/24eca9bc-15f0-11e5-9ddc-e3353542100c_story.html.

14   Moran, Alyssa J., et al. "Increases in Sugary Drink Marketing During Supplemental Nutrition Assistance Program Benefit Issuance in New York." *American Journal of Preventive Medicine*, vol. 55, no. 1, 2018, pp. 55–62, doi:10.1016/j.amepre.2018.03.012.

15   Lin, K. (2019). "Why plastic pollution is an environmental justice issue…"
      Retrieved June 30, 2020, from https://www.greenpeace.org/international
      /story/21792/plastic-waste-environmental-justice/.

16   "Coca-Cola is becoming a serial human rights offender." (2018). Retrieved
      June 30, 2020, from https://www.iufcampaigns.org/campaigns/show
      _campaign.cgi?c=1112.

17   Nace, T. (2019). "Coca-Cola Named The World's Most Polluting Brand…"
      Retrieved June 30, 2020, from https://www.forbes.com/sites/trevornace
      /2019/10/29/coca-cola-named-the-worlds-most-polluting-brand-in-plastic
      -waste-audit/.

18   Shimo, A. (2018). "While Nestlé extracts millions of litres from their
      land… " Retrieved June 30, 2020, from https://www.theguardian.com
      /global/2018/oct/04/ontario-six-nations-nestle-running-water.

19   Richards, R. (2019). "Debunking the Trump Administration's New Water
      Rule…" Retrieved Dec. 4, 2020, from https://www.americanprogress.org
      /issues/green/news/2019/03/27/467697/debunking-trump-administrations
      -new-water-rule/.

20   Oosthoek, Sharon. "Plastic Taints Most Bottled Water, Study Finds."
      Science News for Students, 3 Dec. 2019, www.sciencenewsforstudents.org
      /article/microplastic-taints-most-bottled-water.

21   Lakhani, Nina. "Revealed: Millions of Americans Can't Afford Water as
      Bills Rise 80 percent in a Decade." *The Guardian*, Guardian News and
      Media, June 23, 2020, www.theguardian.com/us-news/2020/jun/23
      /millions-of-americans-cant-afford-water-bills-rise.

22   Deaton, A. (2018). The U.S. Can No Longer Hide From Its Deep Poverty
      Problem. Retrieved December 28, 2020, from https://www.nytimes.com
      /2018/01/24/opinion/poverty-united-states.html.

23   Ingraham, C. (2014). "1.6 million Americans don't have indoor plumbing.
      Here's…" Retrieved December 4, 2020, from https://www.washingtonpost
      .com/news/wonk/wp/2014/04/23/1-6-million-americans-dont-have-indoor
      -plumbing-heres-where-they-live/.

24   Sanders, Bernie, and Brenda Lawrence. "Clean Water Is a Human Right.
      In America It's More a Profit Machine | Bernie Sanders and Brenda
      Lawrence." *The Guardian*, Guardian News and Media, 23 June 2020,
      www.theguardian.com/us-news/commentisfree/2020/jun/23/clean-water
      -should-be-an-american-human-right-not-a-government-profit-machine.

25   A gabion is a cage, cylinder or box filled with rocks, concrete, or sometimes
      sand and soil.

26   See https://www.monolake.org/whatwedo/restoration/ (n.d.). Retrieved
      Nov. 24, 2020, from https://www.monolake.org/whatwedo/restoration/.

27   See the work of Ian Lipsky, Senior Hydrologist at eDesignDynamic.

28   Frankel, J. (2018). *Crisis on the High Plains: The Loss of America's
      Largest Aquifer – the Ogallala.* University of Denver Water Law Review at

the Sturm College of Law. http://duwaterlawreview.com/crisis-on-the-high
-plains-the-loss-of-americas-largest-aquifer-the-ogallala/.

29   See https://www.motherjones.com/environment/2014/08/bottled-water
-california-drought/.

30   Meade, R. H., and J. A. Moody, 1984, *Causes for the decline of
suspended-sediment discharge in the Mississippi River system, 1940–2007*
Hydrology Processes vol. 24, pp. 35–49.

31   Upholt, B. (2019). The Mississippi River Is Under Control—For Now –
Time. Retricved Dec. 4, 2020, from https://time.com/5635375/mississippi
-river-flooding/.

32   "Watershed Academy." Environmental Protection Agency, Feb. 26, 2020,
www.epa.gov/watershedacademy.

33   Valencia, M. (2019). "Officials seek more protections for city wetlands to
counter effects of climate change." Retrieved Dec. 4, 2020, from https:
//www.bostonglobe.com/metro/2019/02/10/officials-seek-more-protections
-for-city-wetlands-counter-effects-climate-change.

34   See http://agris.fao.org/agris-search/search.do?recordID=US201500077447.

35   US EPA (2006). "Economic Benefits of Wetlands." Retrieved Dec. 28, 2020,
from https://www.epa.gov/sites/production/files/2016-02/documents
/economicbenefits.pdf.

36   See http://wedocs.unep.org/bitstream/handle/20.500.11822/19113/
Costanza et_al_GEC_2014_%2B_SI.pdf?sequence=1&isAllowed=y; also
https://voices.nationalgeographic.org/2014/06/24/recent-loss-of-freshwater
-wetlands-worldwide-valued-at-2-7-trillion-per-year/.

37   Gilbreath, A. (n.d.). "Nestlé Is Sucking the World's Aquifers Dry."
Retrieved Dec. 1, 2020, from https://longreads.com/2017/10/04/nestle-is
-sucking-the-worlds-aquifers-dry/.

38   The War on Want (2007, November 19). "Coca-Cola: Drinking the world
dry." Retrieved Dec. 1, 2020, from https://waronwant.org/media/coca
-cola-drinking-world-dry.

39   Times of India (2010, March 18). "Pepsi accused of over extraction of
groundwater." Retrieved Dec. 1, 2020, from https://timesofindia
.indiatimes.com/india/Pepsi-accused-of-over-extraction-of-groundwater
/articleshow/5697895.cms.

40   List of dams and reservoirs in the United States (2021). Retrieved Jan. 27,
2021, from https://en.wikipedia.org/wiki/List_of_dams_and_reservoirs
_in_the_United_States.

41   See https://www.nrcs.usda.gov/Internet/FSE_DOCUMENTS/nrcs144p2
_013673.pdf.

42   See https://www.fema.gov/media-library-data/20130726-1849-25045-6913
/02_hydrosafetydam_ch_2_4.pdf.

43   Rivers, A. *American Rivers Dam Removal Database.* 2, figshare, 13 Nov.
2017, doi:10.6084/m9.figshare.5234068.v2.

44   See http://www.ecosystemmarketplace.com/articles/does-brazilian
      -deforestation-drive-drought-in-the-united-states/; https://www.princeton
      .edu/news/2013/11/07/if-tree-falls-brazil-amazon-deforestation-could
      -mean-droughts-western-us.

45   See https://www.nrdc.org/sites/default/files/bees.pdf.

46   See http://unisoultheory.com/index.php/2016/10/18/trees-feelings
      -communicate/; https://e360.yale.edu/features/exploring_how_and_why
      _trees_talk_to_each_other.

47   See http://www.wri.org/blog/2017/10/global-tree-cover-loss-rose-51
      -percent-2016.

48   See http://www.pbs.org/wgbh/nova/next/nature/47-genes-that-might-help
      -us-help-vulnerable-trees-survive-climate-change/.

49   Knoblauch, Jessica. "Major Victory for Alaska's Majestic Trees and for the
      Climate." Earthjustice, 21 Mar. 2020, earthjustice.org/blog/2019
      -september/tongass-national-forest-victory-old-growth-climate.

50   Kuebler, M. (2020, March 21). "The good news about reforestation
      efforts." Retrieved December 4, 2020, from https://www.dw.com/en
      /nations-world-tackling-deforestation-with-reforestation-world-forest-day.

51   See https://news.nationalgeographic.com/2016/07/india-plants-50-million
      -trees-uttar-pradesh-reforestation/.

52   See https://water.usgs.gov/edu/wateruse-total.html.

53   "Mangroves: Nurseries for the world's seafood supply." IUCN (2017).
      Retrieved Dec. 7, 2020, from https://www.iucn.org/news/forests/201708
      /mangroves-nurseries-world%E2%80%99s-seafood-supply.

54   "The Bridge Between Land and Sea." Earth Island Journal, https://www
      .earthisland.org/journal/index.php/articles/entry/bridge-land-sea
      -mangroves-sri-lanka.

55   Tsang, J. (2020). "How Microbes Clean up Oil: Lessons From the
      Deepwater..." Retrieved Dec. 7, 2020, from https://asm.org/Articles/2020
      /April/How-Microbes-Clean-up-Oil-Lessons-From-the-Deepwat.

56   Beilin, K. (2017). "The World According to Amaranth: Interspecies
      Memory in the Tehuacán Valley." Hispanic Issues Online (24), 141–164.

57   Toledo, Víctor M., and Narciso Barrera-Bassols. "La memoria biocultural:
      La importancia ecológica de las sabidurías tradicionales." Icaria Editorial,
      2008.

58   Lapowsky, I. (n.d.). "Let the Marketplace Solve the Sanitation Crisis."
      Retrieved Nov. 30, 2020, from https://www.inc.com/magazine/201211
      /issie-lapowsky/big-idea-2-marketplace-solve-sanitation-crisis.html.

59   Adelphi research gGmbH (2011). "Waste Enterprises." Retrieved January
      15, 2021, from https://seed.uno/enterprise-profiles/waste-enterprisers.

60   August 5, 2013 · by EEMP Main · in Location of Restoration Projects.
      "Loess Plateau Watershed Rehabilitation Project." Environmental Education
      Media Project (eempc.org/loess-plateau-watershed-rehabilitation-project).

61   Qiao L, Chen W, Wu Y, Liu H, Zhang J, Liu G, Xue S. 2019.
      "Rehabilitation time has greater influences on soil mechanical composition
      and erodibility than does rehabilitation land type in the hilly–gully region
      of the Loess Plateau, China." PeerJ 7:e8090 https://doi.org/10.7717
      /peerj.8090.

62   Rose, S. (2021). "'Our biggest challenge? Lack of imagination': The
      scientists turning the desert green." Retrieved March 22, 2021, from https:
      //www.theguardian.com/environment/2021/mar/20/our-biggest-challenge
      -lack-of-imagination-the-scientists-turning-the-desert-green.

63   "Elwha River Restoration." National Parks Service. U.S. Department of
      the Interior, n.d. Web. 04 May 2020.

64   *Records of the Colony of Rhode Island and Providence Plantations*; vol. 1,
      16th March, 1639.

65   Rotkin-Ellman, M., Jahshan, et al. (2016, Dec. 15). *Reduce Fracking
      Health Hazards.* NRDC. https://www.nrdc.org/issues/reduce-fracking
      -health-hazards.

66   Murphy, D. (2020, September 22). The Fight to Keep the Kruščica River
      Wild. Rewild.org. Retrieved September 29, 2021, from https://www.rewild
      .org/news/the-fight-to-keep-the-kruscica-river-wild.

67   Rochat, Ezekiel. "Roof Types for Rainwater Harvesting: PerfectWater™."
      PerfectWater, Sept. 13, 2018, 4perfectwater.com/blog/rainwater-harvesting
      -roof-types/.

68   Stoner, Nancy. "Bring Back the Water Fountain." *The EPA Blog*,
      Environmental Protection Agency, 14 Feb. 2012, blog.epa.gov/2012/02/14
      /bring-back-the-water-fountain-2/.

69   Pierre-Louis, Kendra. "We Don't Trust Drinking Fountains Anymore, and
      That's Bad for Our Health." *The Washington Post*, WP Company, July 8,
      2015, www.washingtonpost.com/opinions/we-dont-trust-drinking
      -fountains-anymore.

Printed in the USA
CPSIA information can be obtained
at www.ICGtesting.com
CBHW061633150724
11608CB00017B/584